A Review
of Geometry

Richard N. Aufmann
Palomar College, CA

Vernon C. Barker
Palomar College, CA

Joanne S. Lockwood
Plymouth State College, NH

Houghton Mifflin Company   **Boston**   **Toronto**

Dallas   Geneva, Illinois   Palo Alto   Princeton, New Jersey

Sponsoring Editor: Maureen O'Connor
Senior Development Editor: Tony Palermino
Senior Project Editor: Toni Haluga
Senior Production/Design Coordinator: Patricia Mahtani
Manufacturing Coordinator: Holly Schuster
Marketing Manager: Michael Ginley

Cover concept and design: Catherine Hawkes

Printed in the U.S.A.

ISBN Numbers:
Text: 0-395-57899-x
Answer Pamphlet: 0-395-66718-6

12345678-CS-97 96 95 94 93

CONTENTS

PREFACE

A Review of Geometry is an informal examination of the geometry topics considered essential for success in mathematics. It was designed to enhance the coverage of geometry topics that are explored in the textbooks by Aufmann/Barker/Lockwood. However, *A Review of Geometry* will complement the needs of instructors who are using alternate materials.

Features

The Interactive Approach

A Review of Geometry uses an interactive style that provides a student with an opportunity to try a skill as it is presented. Each section is divided into objectives, and every objective contains one or more sets of matched-pair examples. The first example in each set is worked out; the second example is not. By solving this second problem, the student interacts with the text. There are complete, worked-out solutions to these examples in an appendix at the end of the book, so the student can obtain immediate feedback on and reinforcement of the skill being learned.

Emphasis on Problem-Solving Strategies

Besides a presentation of the fundamental geometry concepts, *A Review of Geometry* contains an abundant number of applications of geometry. Each application problem features a carefully developed approach to problem solving that emphasizes developing strategies to solve problems. Students are encouraged to develop their own strategies and to write these strategies as part of the solution to a problem.

Exercises

End-of-Section Exercises

There are a wide variety of exercise sets in *A Review of Geometry*. At the end of each section are exercise sets that are keyed to the corresponding learning objective. The exercises are carefully developed to ensure that students can apply the concepts to a variety of problem-solving situations.

It is assumed that the student will use a calculator to solve many of the exercises in *A Review of Geometry*. For example, in Section 4, a scientific calculator is used to find approximate values in calculations involving π.

Supplemental Exercises

The end-of-section exercises are followed by Supplemental Exercises. These exercises require that a student investigate a certain concept in more depth or detail. Interspersed throughout the Supplemental Exercises are Writing Exercises, designated by a $\boxed{w}$. These exercises ask students to write a few paragraphs about a topic presented in the section or to research and report on a related topic.

Answers to the odd-numbered exercises are provided in the appendix.

Acknowledgements

The authors would like to thank the people who have reviewed this manuscript and provided many valuable suggestions:

Cindy Moody
City College of San Francisco

Karen Schwitters
Seminole Community College

Jean Woody
Tulsa Junior College

A Review of Geometry

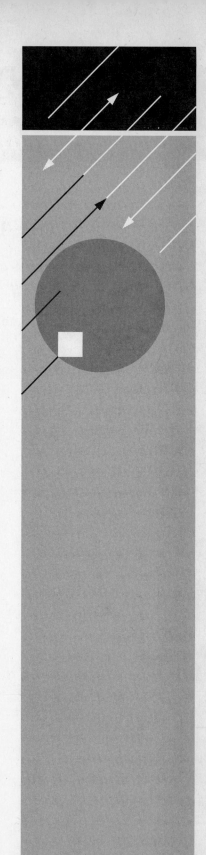

1 Introduction to Geometry

- **A** Problems involving lines and angles
- **B** Problems involving angles formed by intersecting lines
- **C** Problems involving the angles of a triangle

2 Polygons

- **A** Problems involving polygons
- **B** Perimeter of a polygon
- **C** Area of a polygon

3 Triangles

- **A** Right triangles
- **B** Similar triangles
- **C** Congruent triangles

4 Circles

- **A** Circumference and area of a circle

5 Solids

- **A** Volume of a solid
- **B** Surface area of a solid

6 Composite Figures

- **A** Perimeter of a composite plane figure
- **B** Area of a composite plane figure
- **C** Volume of a composite solid
- **D** Surface area of a composite solid

Measurement

A geometric figure is described by its shape and its size. The name of a figure can describe its shape, for example, line segment, circle, or cube. The size of a figure must be described by giving a measure. A **measure** is a number accompanied by a unit of measure; for example, 28 feet and 16 meters are measures.

An angle is a geometric figure. One unit of measure that is used to describe the size of an angle is the degree, which is described in Section 1. Three other types of units of measure that are used to describe the size of a geometric figure are units of length, units of area, and units of volume.

Units of length, area, and volume may be given in either the United States Customary System of measurement or the metric system of measurement. In this booklet, the units of measure are given as abbreviations. The lists below provide the standard abbreviations for units of measure in each system of measurement.

1. **Units of length**

    Units of length are used to describe distance.
    Distance has only one dimension—length. It has no width or height.

U.S. Customary System		Metric System	
in.	inches	mm	millimeters
ft	feet	cm	centimeters
yd	yards	m	meters
mi	miles	km	kilometers

2. **Units of area**

    Units of area are used to describe the amount of surface in a region.
    Area has two dimensions—length and width.
    Units of area can always be expressed in terms of a unit of length squared.

U.S. Customary System		Metric System	
in^2	square inches	mm^2	square millimeters
ft^2	square feet	cm^2	square centimeters
yd^2	square yards	m^2	square meters
mi^2	square miles	km^2	square kilometers

3. **Units of volume**

    Units of volume are used to describe the amount of space occupied by a solid.
    Volume has three dimensions—length, width, and height.
    Units of volume can always be expressed in terms of a unit of length cubed.

U.S. Customary System		Metric System	
in^3	cubic inches	mm^3	cubic millimeters
ft^3	cubic feet	cm^3	cubic centimeters
yd^3	cubic yards	m^3	cubic meters

SECTION 1 Introduction to Geometry

OBJECTIVE **A**   **Problems involving lines and angles**

The word *geometry* comes from the Greek words for "earth" and "measure." The original purpose of geometry was to measure land. Today, geometry is used in many fields, such as physics, medicine, and geology. Geometry is used in applied fields such as mechanical drawing and astronomy. Geometric form is used in art and design.

Three basic concepts of geometry are point, line, and plane. A **point** is symbolized by drawing a dot. A **line** is determined by two distinct points and extends indefinitely in both directions, as the arrows on the line shown at the right indicate. This line contains points *A* and *B* and is represented by $\overleftrightarrow{AB}$. A line can also be represented by a single letter, such as *l*.

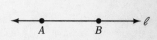

Any point on a line separates the line into three parts: the point and two **half-lines**. A half-line extends indefinitely in one direction.

The half-line shown at the right is symbolized by $\overset{\circ}{CD}$, where the open circle indicates that point *C* is not included in the half-line. Point *C* is called the **endpoint** of the half-line.

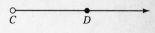

A **ray** is a half-line that includes its endpoint. The ray shown at the right is denoted by $\overrightarrow{AB}$.

A **line segment** is a part of a line that has two endpoints. The line segment shown at the right is denoted by $\overline{AB}$.

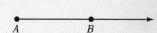

The distance between the endpoints of $\overline{AC}$ is denoted by *AC*. If *B* is a point on $\overline{AC}$, then *AC* (the distance from *A* to *C*) is the sum of *AB* (the distance from *A* to *B*) and *BC* (the distance from *B* to *C*).

AC = AB + BC

Given *AB* = 22 cm and *AC* = 31 cm, find *BC*.

Write an equation for the distances between points on the line segment.   *AC = AB + BC*

Substitute the given distances for *AB* and *AC* into the equation. $31 = 22 + BC$

Solve for *BC*. $9 = BC$

BC = 9 cm

In this section we will be discussing figures that lie in a plane. **A plane** is a flat surface and can be pictured as a table top or blackboard that extends in all directions.

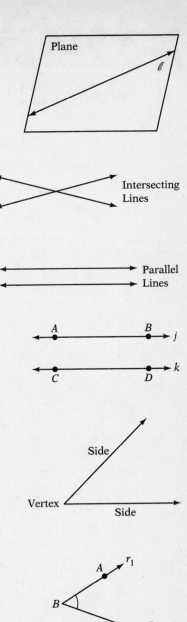

A line in a plane separates the plane into three parts: the line and two **half-planes**. In the figure at the right above, line l separates plane P into two half-planes.

Lines in a plane can be intersecting or parallel. **Intersecting lines** cross at a point in the plane. **Parallel lines** never meet. The distance between them is always the same.

The symbol $\parallel$ means "is parallel to." In the figure at the right, $j \parallel k$ and $\overline{AB} \parallel \overline{CD}$. Note that j contains $\overline{AB}$ and k contains $\overline{CD}$. Parallel lines contain parallel line segments.

An **angle** is formed by two rays with the same endpoint. The **vertex** of the angle is the point at which the two rays meet. The rays are called the **sides** of the angle.

If A and C are points on rays r_1 and r_2, and B is the vertex, then the angle is called $\angle B$ or $\angle ABC$, where $\angle$ is the symbol for angle. Note that the angle is named by the vertex, or the vertex is the second point listed when the angle is named by giving three points. $\angle ABC$ could also be called $\angle CBA$.

An angle can also be named by a variable written between the rays close to the vertex. In the figure at the right, $\angle x = \angle QRS$ and $\angle y = \angle SRT$. Note that in this figure, more than two rays meet at R. In this case, the vertex cannot be used to name an angle.

An angle is measured in **degrees**. The symbol for degrees is a small raised circle, °. Probably because early Babylonians believed that Earth revolves around the sun in approximately 360 days, the angle formed by a circle has a measure of 360° (360 degrees).

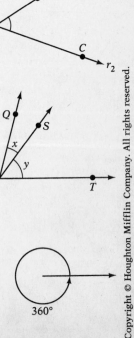

A **protractor** is used to measure an angle. Place the center of the protractor at the vertex of the angle with the edge of the protractor along a side of the angle. The angle shown in the figure below measures 58°.

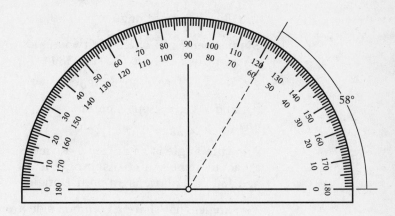

A 90° angle is called a **right angle.** The symbol ⌐ represents a right angle.

Perpendicular lines are intersecting lines that form right angles.

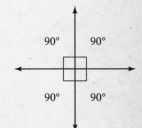

The symbol ⊥ means "is perpendicular to." In the figure at the right, $p \perp q$ and $\overline{AB} \perp \overline{CD}$. Note that line p contains $\overline{AB}$ and line q contains $\overline{CD}$. Perpendicular lines contain perpendicular line segments.

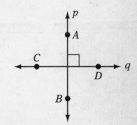

Two lines that are perpendicular to a given line are parallel to each other. In the figure at the right, $l_1 \perp l$ and $l_2 \perp l$; therefore, $l_1 \parallel l_2$.

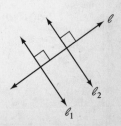

Complementary angles are two angles whose measures have the sum 90°.

$\angle A + \angle B = 70° + 20° = 90°$

$\angle A$ and $\angle B$ are complementary angles.

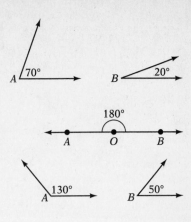

A 180° angle is called a **straight angle.**

$\angle AOB$ is a straight angle.

Supplementary angles are two angles whose measures have the sum 180°.

$\angle A + \angle B = 130° + 50° = 180°$

$\angle A$ and $\angle B$ are supplementary angles.

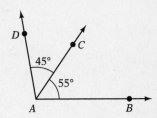

An **acute angle** is an angle whose measure is between 0° and 90°. $\angle B$ above is an acute angle. An **obtuse angle** is an angle whose measure is between 90° and 180°. $\angle A$ above is an obtuse angle.

Two angles that share a common side are **adjacent angles.** In the figure at the right, $\angle DAC$ and $\angle CAB$ are adjacent angles. $\angle DAC = 45°$ and $\angle CAB = 55°$.

$$\angle DAB = \angle DAC + \angle CAB$$
$$= 45° + 55° = 100°$$

In the figure at the right, $\angle EDG = 80°$. $\angle FDG$ is three times the measure of $\angle EDF$. Find the measure of $\angle EDF$.

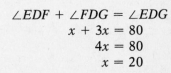

Let x = the measure of $\angle EDF$.
Then $3x$ = the measure of $\angle FDG$.
Write an equation and solve for x, the measure of $\angle EDF$.

$$\angle EDF + \angle FDG = \angle EDG$$
$$x + 3x = 80$$
$$4x = 80$$
$$x = 20$$

$\angle EDF = 20°$

Example 1   Given $MN = 15$ mm, $NO = 18$ mm, and $MP = 48$ mm, find OP.

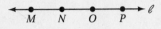

Solution $MN + NO + OP = MP$
$15 + 18 + OP = 48$
$33 + OP = 48$
$OP = 15$

$OP = 15$ mm

Example 2   Given $QR = 24$ cm, $ST = 17$ cm, and $QT = 62$ cm, find RS.

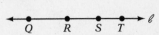

Your Solution

Solution on p. A3

Example 3 Given $XY = 9$ m and YZ is twice XY, find XZ.

Solution $XZ = XY + YZ$
$XZ = XY + 2(XY)$
$XZ = 9 + 2(9)$
$XZ = 9 + 18$
$XZ = 27$

$XZ = 27$ m

Example 4 Given $BC = 16$ ft and $AB = \dfrac{1}{4}(BC)$, find AC.

Your Solution

Example 5 Find the complement of a 43° angle.

Strategy Complementary angles are two angles whose sum is 90°. To find the complement, let x represent the complement of a 43° angle. Write an equation and solve for x.

Solution $x + 43° = 90°$
$\quad\quad\ x = 47°$

The complement of a 43° angle is a 47° angle.

Example 6 Find the supplement of a 129° angle.

Your Strategy

Your Solution

Example 7 Find the measure of $\angle x$.

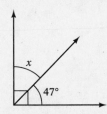

Strategy To find the measure of $\angle x$, write an equation using the fact that the sum of the measure of $\angle x$ and 47° is 90°. Solve for $\angle x$.

Solution $\angle x + 47° = 90°$
$\quad\quad\ \angle x = 43°$

The measure of $\angle x$ is 43°.

Example 8 Find the measure of $\angle a$.

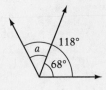

Your Strategy

Your Solution

Solutions on p. A3

OBJECTIVE **B** Problems involving angles formed by intersecting lines

Four angles are formed by the intersection of two lines. If the two lines are perpendicular, each of the four angles is a right angle. If the two lines are not perpendicular, then two of the angles formed are acute angles and two of the angles are obtuse angles. The two acute angles are always opposite each other, and the two obtuse angles are always opposite each other.

In the figure at the right, $\angle w$ and $\angle y$ are acute angles. $\angle x$ and $\angle z$ are obtuse angles.

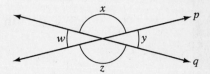

Two angles that are on opposite sides of the intersection of two lines are called **vertical angles.** Vertical angles have the same measure. $\angle w$ and $\angle y$ are vertical angles. $\angle x$ and $\angle z$ are vertical angles.

Vertical angles have the same measure.

$$\angle w = \angle y$$
$$\angle x = \angle z$$

Two angles that share a common side are called **adjacent angles.** For the figure shown above, $\angle x$ and $\angle y$ are adjacent angles, as are $\angle y$ and $\angle z$, $\angle z$ and $\angle w$, and $\angle w$ and $\angle x$. Adjacent angles of intersecting lines are supplementary angles.

Adjacent angles of intersecting lines are supplementary angles.

$$\angle x + \angle y = 180°$$
$$\angle y + \angle z = 180°$$
$$\angle z + \angle w = 180°$$
$$\angle w + \angle x = 180°$$

Given that $\angle c = 65°$, find the measures of angles a, b, and d.

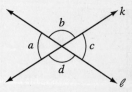

$\angle c = \angle a$ because $\angle c$ and $\angle a$ are vertical angles.

$$\angle a = 65°$$

$\angle c$ is supplementary to $\angle b$ because $\angle c$ and $\angle b$ are adjacent angles of intersecting lines.

$$\angle c + \angle b = 180°$$
$$65° + \angle b = 180°$$
$$\angle b = 115°$$

$\angle b = \angle d$ because $\angle b$ and $\angle d$ are vertical angles.

$$\angle d = 115°$$

A line that intersects two other lines at different points is called a **transversal**.

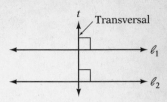

If the lines cut by a transversal t are parallel lines and the transversal is perpendicular to the parallel lines, all eight angles formed are right angles.

If the lines cut by a transversal t are parallel lines and the transversal is not perpendicular to the parallel lines, all four acute angles have the same measure and all four obtuse angles have the same measure. For the figure at the right,

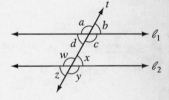

$\angle b = \angle d = \angle x = \angle z$

$\angle a = \angle c = \angle w = \angle y$

Alternate interior angles are two angles that are on opposite sides of a transversal and between the parallel lines. In the figure above, $\angle c$ and $\angle w$ are alternate interior angles; $\angle d$ and $\angle x$ are alternate interior angles. Alternate interior angles have the same measure.

Alternate interior angles have the same measure.

$\angle c = \angle w$
$\angle d = \angle x$

Alternate exterior angles are two angles that are on opposite sides of a transversal and outside the parallel lines. In the figure above, $\angle a$ and $\angle y$ are alternate exterior angles; $\angle b$ and $\angle z$ are alternate exterior angles. Alternate exterior angles have the same measure.

Alternate exterior angles have the same measure.

$\angle a = \angle y$
$\angle b = \angle z$

Corresponding angles are two angles that are on the same side of a transversal and are both acute angles or both obtuse angles. For the figure above, the following pairs of angles are corresponding angles: $\angle a$ and $\angle w$, $\angle d$ and $\angle z$, $\angle b$ and $\angle x$, $\angle c$ and $\angle y$. Corresponding angles have the same measure.

Corresponding angles have the same measure.

$\angle a = \angle w$
$\angle d = \angle z$
$\angle b = \angle x$
$\angle c = \angle y$

■ Given that $l_1 \parallel l_2$ and $\angle c = 58°$, find the measures of $\angle f$, $\angle h$, and $\angle g$.

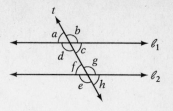

$\angle c$ and $\angle f$ are alternate interior angles.

$\angle c$ and $\angle h$ are corresponding angles.

$\angle g$ is supplementary to $\angle h$.

$\angle f = \angle c = 58°$

$\angle h = \angle c = 58°$

$\angle g + \angle h = 180°$
$\angle g + 58° = 180°$
$\angle g = 122°$

Example 9 Find x.

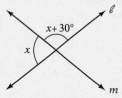

Example 10 Find x.

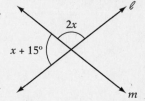

Strategy The angles labeled are adjacent angles of intersecting lines and are, therefore, supplementary angles. To find x, write an equation and solve for x.

Your Strategy

Solution $x + (x + 30°) = 180°$
$\qquad\quad 2x + 30° = 180°$
$\qquad\qquad\quad 2x = 150°$
$\qquad\qquad\quad\; x = 75°$

Your Solution

Example 11 Given $l_1 \parallel l_2$, find x.

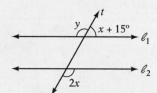

Example 12 Given $l_1 \parallel l_2$, find x.

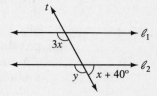

Strategy $2x = y$ because alternate exterior angles have the same measure. $(x + 15°) + y = 180°$ because adjacent angles of intersecting lines are supplementary angles. Substitute $2x$ for y and solve for x.

Your Strategy

Solution $(x + 15°) + 2x = 180°$
$\qquad\quad 3x + 15° = 180°$
$\qquad\qquad\quad 3x = 165°$
$\qquad\qquad\quad\; x = 55°$

Your Solution

Solutions on p. A3

OBJECTIVE C   Problems involving the angles of a triangle

If the lines cut by a transversal are not parallel lines, the three lines will intersect at three points. In the figure at the right, the transversal *t* intersects lines *p* and *q*. The three lines intersect at points *A*, *B*, and *C*. These three points define three line segments, $\overline{AB}$, $\overline{BC}$, and $\overline{AC}$. The plane figure formed by these three line segments is called a **triangle**.

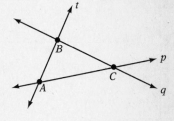

Each of the three points of intersection is the vertex of four angles. The angles within the region enclosed by the triangle are called **interior angles.** In the figure at the right, angles *a*, *b*, and *c* are interior angles. The sum of the measures of the interior angles is 180°.

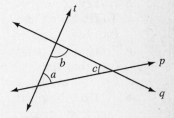

The sum of the measures of the interior angles of a triangle is 180°.

$$\angle a + \angle b + \angle c = 180°$$

An angle adjacent to an interior angle is an **exterior angle.** In the figure at the right, angles *m* and *n* are exterior angles for angle *a*. The sum of the measures of an interior and an exterior angle is 180°.

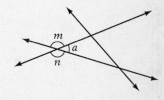

The sum of the measures of an interior and an exterior angle is 180°.

$$\angle a + \angle m = 180°$$
$$\angle a + \angle n = 180°$$

Given that $\angle c = 40°$ and $\angle g = 100°$, find the measure of $\angle y$.

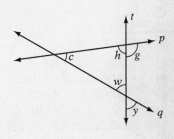

$\angle g$ and $\angle h$ are supplementary angles.

$$\angle g + \angle h = 180°$$
$$100° + \angle h = 180°$$
$$\angle h = 80°$$

The sum of the interior angles is 180°.

$$\angle c + \angle h + \angle w = 180°$$
$$40° + 80° + \angle w = 180°$$
$$120° + \angle w = 180°$$
$$\angle w = 60°$$

$\angle w$ and $\angle y$ are vertical angles.

$$\angle y = \angle w = 60°$$

Example 13

Given that $\angle y = 55°$, find the measures of angles a, b, and d.

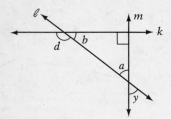

Strategy

▶ To find the measure of angle a, use the fact that $\angle a$ and $\angle y$ are vertical angles.
▶ To find the measure of angle b, use the fact that the sum of the measures of the interior angles of a triangle is 180°.
▶ To find the measure of angle d, use the fact that the sum of an interior and an exterior angle is 180°.

Solution

$\angle a = \angle y = 55°$

$\angle a + \angle b + 90° = 180°$
$55° + \angle b + 90° = 180°$
$\quad\quad \angle b + 145° = 180°$
$\quad\quad\quad\quad\quad \angle b = 35°$

$\angle d + \angle b = 180°$
$\angle d + 35° = 180°$
$\quad\quad \angle d = 145°$

Example 15

Two angles of a triangle measure 53° and 78°. Find the measure of the third angle.

Strategy

To find the measure of the third angle, use the fact that the sum of the measures of the interior angles of a triangle is 180°. Write an equation using x to represent the measure of the third angle. Solve the equation for x.

Solution

$x + 53° + 78° = 180°$
$\quad\quad x + 131° = 180°$
$\quad\quad\quad\quad\quad x = 49°$

The measure of the third angle is 49°.

Example 14

Given that $\angle a = 45°$ and $\angle x = 100°$, find the measures of angles b, c, and y.

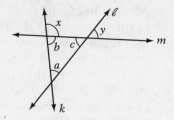

Your Strategy

Your Solution

Example 16

One angle in a triangle is a right angle, and one angle measures 34°. Find the measure of the third angle.

Your Strategy

Your Solution

1 EXERCISES

▶ **Objective A**

Use a protractor to measure the angle. State whether the angle is acute, obtuse, or right.

1.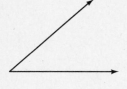

2.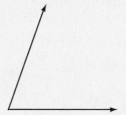

3.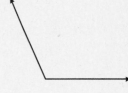

4.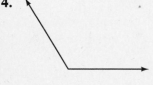

5.

6.

Solve.

7. Find the complement of a 62° angle.

8. Find the complement of a 31° angle.

9. Find the supplement of a 162° angle.

10. Find the supplement of a 72° angle.

11. Given $AB = 12$ cm, $CD = 9$ cm, and $AD = 35$ cm, find the length of BC.

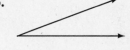

12. Given $AB = 21$ mm, $BC = 14$ mm, and $AD = 54$ mm, find the length of CD.

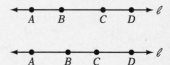

13. Given $QR = 7$ ft and RS is three times the length of QR, find the length of QS.

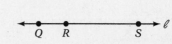

14. Given $QR = 15$ in. and RS is twice the length of QR, find the length of QS.

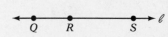

15. Given $EF = 20$ m and FG is $\frac{1}{2}$ the length of EF, find the length of EG.

16. Given $EF = 18$ cm and FG is $\frac{1}{3}$ the length of EF, find the length of EG.

Solve.

17. Given ∠*LOM* = 53° and ∠*LON* = 139°, find the measure of ∠*MON*.

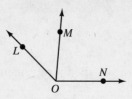

18. Given ∠*MON* = 38° and ∠*LON* = 85°, find the measure of ∠*LOM*.

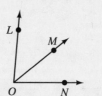

Find the measure of ∠*x*.

19.

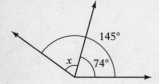

20.

Given that ∠*LON* is a right angle, find the measure of ∠*x*.

21.

22.

23.

24.

Find the measure of ∠*a*.

25.

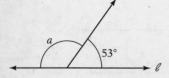

26.

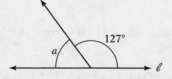

27.

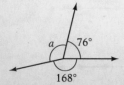

28.

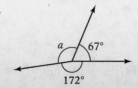

Find *x*.

29.
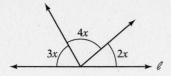

30.
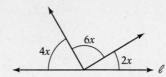

31.
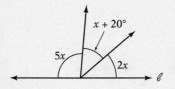

32.
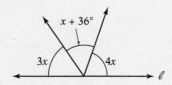

33.

34.

35. Given ∠*a* = 51°, find the measure of ∠*b*.

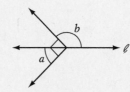

36. Given ∠*a* = 38°, find the measure of ∠*b*.

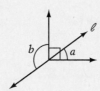

▶ **Objective B**

Find the measure of ∠*x*.

37.
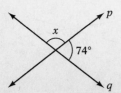

38.
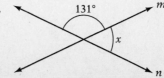

Find x.

39.

40.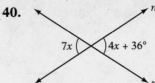

Given that $l_1 \parallel l_2$, find the measures of angles a and b.

41.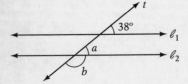

42.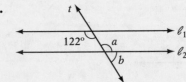

43.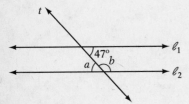

44.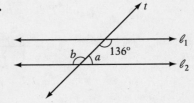

Given that $l_1 \parallel l_2$, find x.

45.

46.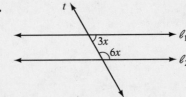

47.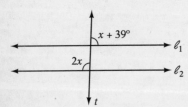

48.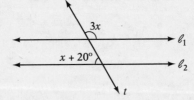

▶ **Objective C**

Solve.

49. Given that $\angle a = 95°$ and $\angle b = 70°$, find the measures of angles x and y.

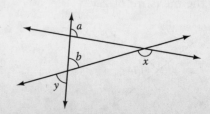

Solve.

50. Given that ∠a = 35° and ∠b = 55°, find the measures of angles *x* and *y*.

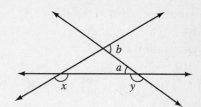

51. Given that ∠y = 45°, find the measures of angles *a* and *b*.

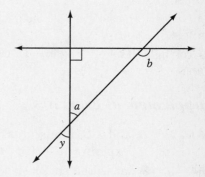

52. Given that ∠y = 130°, find the measures of angles *a* and *b*.

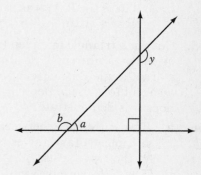

53. Given that $\overline{AO} \perp \overline{OB}$, express in terms of *x* the number of degrees in ∠*BOC*.

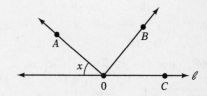

54. Given that $\overline{AO} \perp \overline{OB}$, express in terms of *x* the number of degrees in ∠*AOC*.

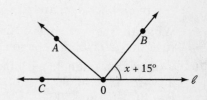

55. One angle in a triangle is a right angle, and one angle is equal to 30°. What is the measure of the other angle?

56. A triangle has one right angle and one angle equal to 7°. What is the measure of the third angle?

Solve.

57. Two angles of a triangle measure 42° and 103°. Find the measure of the third angle.

58. Two angles of a triangle measure 62° and 45°. Find the measure of the third angle.

59. A triangle has a 13° angle and a 65° angle. What is the measure of the other angle?

60. A triangle has a 105° angle and a 32° angle. What is the measure of the other angle?

61. A triangle has a 45° angle and a right angle. Find the measure of the other angle.

62. A triangle has a 60° angle and a right angle. Find the measure of the other angle.

▶ *Supplemental Exercises*

w **63.** If $\overline{AB}$ and $\overline{CD}$ intersect at point O, and $\angle AOC = \angle BOC$, explain why $\overline{AB} \perp \overline{CD}$.

64. **a.** What is the smallest possible whole number of degrees in an angle of a triangle?
b. What is the largest possible whole number of degrees in an angle of a triangle?

w **65.** Cut out a triangle and then tear off two of the angles, as shown at the right. Position the pieces you tore off so that angle a is adjacent to angle b and angle c is adjacent to angle b. Describe what you observe. What does this demonstrate?

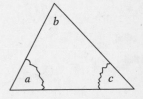

66. **a.** The difference between the measures of two complementary angles is 10°. Find the measures of the two angles.
b. The difference between the measures of two supplementary angles is 20°. Find the measures of the two angles.

67. For the figure at the right, find the sum of the measures of angles x, y, and z.

w **68.** For the figure at the right, explain why $\angle a + \angle b = \angle x$. Write a rule that describes the relationship between an exterior angle of a triangle and the opposite interior angles. Use the rule to write an equation involving angles a, c, and z.

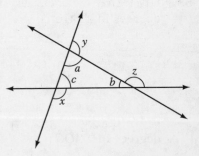

w **69.** What are the meanings of the words "acute" and "obtuse" in describing a person?

70. Construct a triangle with the given angle measures.
a. 45°, 45°, and 90°   **b.** 30°, 60°, and 90°
c. 40°, 40°, and 100°

71. Determine whether each statement is always true, sometimes true, or never true.
a. Two lines that are parallel to a third line are parallel to each other.
b. A triangle contains two acute angles.
c. Vertical angles are complementary angles.

w **72.** Do some research on the principle of reflection. Explain how this principle applies to the operation of a periscope and to the game of billiards.

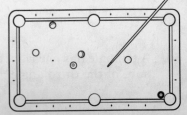

SECTION 2 Polygons

OBJECTIVE A   Problems involving polygons

A **polygon** is a closed figure determined by three or more line segments that lie in a plane. The line segments that form the polygon are called its **sides**. The figures below are examples of polygons.

      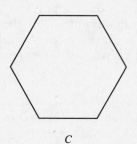   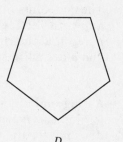   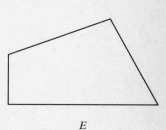

A regular polygon is one in which each side has the same length. The polygons in Figures A, C, and D above are regular polygons.

A **regular polygon** is one in which each side has the same length. The polygons in Figures A, C, and D above are regular polygons.

The polygons in Figures F and I below are **convex polygons.** A convex polygon is one in which no line containing a side of the polygon will intersect another side of the polygon. The polygons in Figures G and H are not convex polygons because a line can be drawn that contains one side of the polygon and intersects another side of the polygon.

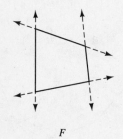   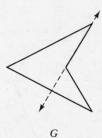   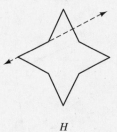   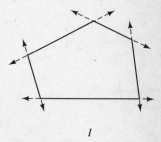

In this text, the discussion of polygons will be restricted to convex polygons.

The name of a polygon is based on the number of sides it has. The table below lists the names of polygons that have from 3 to 10 sides.

Number of Sides	Name of the Polygon
3	Triangle
4	Quadrilateral
5	Pentagon
6	Hexagon
7	Heptagon
8	Octagon
9	Nonagon
10	Decagon

A **vertex** of a polygon is a point at which two line segments meet. An angle at the vertex of a polygon is called an **interior angle.** An **exterior angle** is an angle that is adjacent to an interior angle. Corresponding interior and exterior angles are supplementary angles.

For the polygon at the right, a corresponding exterior angle for each of the interior angles, angles *a*, *b*, *c*, *d*, and *e*, is shown.

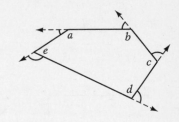

The endpoints of one side of a polygon are **adjacent vertices.** For example, for the polygon at the right, the vertices of angles *a* and *b* are adjacent vertices of the polygon.

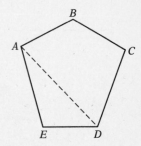

A **diagonal** of a polygon is a line segment joining two nonadjacent vertices. $\overline{AD}$ is a diagonal for the polygon at the right.

The sum of the interior angles of a triangle is 180°. Using this fact, a formula can be developed for the sum of the interior angles of any convex polygon. Four polygons are shown below. Using vertex *A*, all of the possible diagonals for each polygon are drawn. Each of the diagonals forms a triangle within the polygon. Note that, in each polygon, the number of triangles formed is two less than the number of sides.

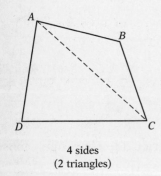

4 sides
(2 triangles)

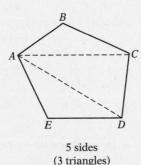

5 sides
(3 triangles)

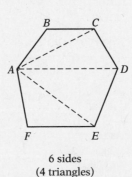

6 sides
(4 triangles)

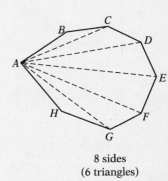

8 sides
(6 triangles)

Since the sum of the interior angles of each triangle is 180°, the sum of the interior angles of a convex polygon is the product of the number of triangles and 180°. This is expressed in the following formula.

> ### Sum of the Measures of the Interior Angles of a Polygon
>
> The sum of the measures of the interior angles of a polygon with *n* sides is $(n - 2)180°$.

▮ Find the sum of the measures of the interior angles of a heptagon.

Use the formula for the sum of the measures $(n - 2)180°$
of the interior angles of a polygon. $(7 - 2)180°$
A heptagon has 7 sides; $n = 7$. $(5)180°$
                                                      $900°$

The sum of the measures of the interior angles of a heptagon is 900°.

Triangles and quadrilaterals are two of the most common types of polygons. Triangles are distinguished by the number of equal sides and also by the measures of their angles.

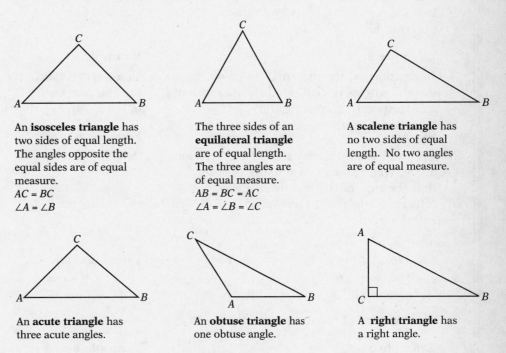

An **isosceles triangle** has two sides of equal length. The angles opposite the equal sides are of equal measure.
$AC = BC$
$\angle A = \angle B$

The three sides of an **equilateral triangle** are of equal length. The three angles are of equal measure.
$AB = BC = AC$
$\angle A = \angle B = \angle C$

A **scalene triangle** has no two sides of equal length. No two angles are of equal measure.

An **acute triangle** has three acute angles.

An **obtuse triangle** has one obtuse angle.

A **right triangle** has a right angle.

Quadrilaterals are also distinguished by their sides and angles, as shown below. Note that a rectangle, a square, and a rhombus are different forms of a parallelogram.

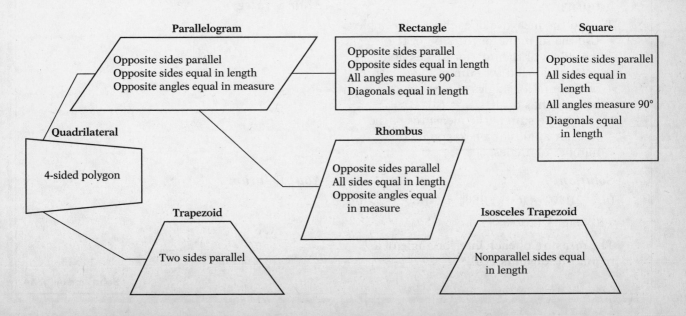

Parallelogram
Opposite sides parallel
Opposite sides equal in length
Opposite angles equal in measure

Rectangle
Opposite sides parallel
Opposite sides equal in length
All angles measure 90°
Diagonals equal in length

Square
Opposite sides parallel
All sides equal in length
All angles measure 90°
Diagonals equal in length

Quadrilateral
4-sided polygon

Rhombus
Opposite sides parallel
All sides equal in length
Opposite angles equal in measure

Trapezoid
Two sides parallel

Isosceles Trapezoid
Nonparallel sides equal in length

Example 1

Which of the figures below is a polygon?

A   B   C

Solution

Figure *A* is not closed and, therefore, is not a polygon. Figure *B* contains intersecting line segments and, therefore, is not a polygon. Figure *C* is a polygon.

Example 3

In a pentagon, the measure of one of the interior angles is 120°. Find the measure of a corresponding exterior angle.

Strategy

Let *x* represent the measure of the exterior angle. Write an equation using the fact that the sum of the measures of an interior angle and a corresponding exterior angle is 180°. Solve the equation for *x*.

Solution

$x + 120° = 180°$
$\quad\quad x = 60°$

The measure of the exterior angle is 60°.

Example 5

Find the measure of each interior angle of a regular hexagon.

Strategy

To find the measure of each interior angle:
▶ Use the formula for the sum of the measures of the interior angles of a polygon to find the sum of the measures of the interior angles of a hexagon. A hexagon has 6 sides; $n = 6$.
▶ Divide the sum of the measures of the interior angles of a hexagon by the number of angles, 6.

Solution

$(n - 2)180° = (6 - 2)180° = (4)180° = 720°$

$720° \div 6 = 120°$

The measure of each interior angle of a regular hexagon is 120°.

Example 2

Which of the figures below is a polygon?

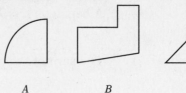

A   B   C

Your Solution

Example 4

In a quadrilateral, the measure of one of the interior angles is 98°. Find the measure of a corresponding exterior angle.

Your Strategy

Your Solution

Example 6

Find the measure of each interior angle of a regular dodecagon (a 12-sided polygon).

Your Strategy

Your Solution

Solutions on p. A4

OBJECTIVE ▉B   Perimeter of a polygon

The **perimeter** of a plane geometric figure is a measure of the distance around the figure. Perimeter is used in buying fencing for a lawn or determining how much baseboard is needed for a room.

The perimeter of a triangle is the sum of the lengths of the three sides.

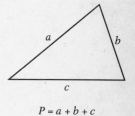

Perimeter of a Triangle

Let a, b, and c be the lengths of the sides of a triangle. The perimeter, P, of the triangle is given by $P = a + b + c$.

$$P = a + b + c$$

Find the perimeter of the triangle shown at the right.

$$P = 5 + 7 + 10 = 22$$

The perimeter is 22 ft.

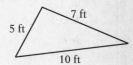

The perimeter of a quadrilateral is the sum of the lengths of its four sides.

A rectangle is a quadrilateral with opposite sides of equal length. Usually the length, L, of a rectangle refers to the length of one of the longer sides of the rectangle and the width, W, refers to the length of one of the shorter sides. The perimeter can then be represented as $P = L + W + L + W$.

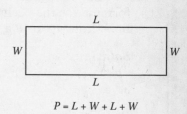

$$P = L + W + L + W$$

The formula for the perimeter of a rectangle is derived by combining like terms.

$$P = 2L + 2W$$

Perimeter of a Rectangle

Let L represent the length and W the width of a rectangle. The perimeter, P, of the rectangle is given by $P = 2L + 2W$.

Find the perimeter of the rectangle shown at the right.

The length is 5 m. Substitute 5 for L. $P = 2L + 2W$
The width is 2 m. Substitute 2 for W. $P = 2(5) + 2(2)$
Solve for P. $P = 10 + 4$
     $P = 14$

The perimeter is 14 m.

A square is a rectangle in which each side has the same length. Letting *s* represent the length of each side of a square, the perimeter of a square can be represented $P = S + S + S + S$.

The formula for the perimeter of a square is derived by combining like terms.

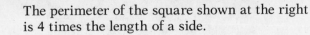

$P = s + s + s + s$

$P = 4s$

Perimeter of a Square

Let *s* represent the length of a side of a square.
The perimeter, *P*, of the square is given by $P = 4s$.

The perimeter of the square shown at the right is 4 times the length of a side.

$$P = 4s = 4(8) = 32$$

The perimeter is 32 in.

8 in.

Example 7

A carpenter is designing a square patio with a perimeter of 44 ft. What is the length of each side?

Strategy

To find the length of each side, use the formula for the perimeter of a square. Substitute 44 for *P* and solve for *s*.

Solution

$P = 4s$
$44 = 4s$
$11 = s$

The length of each side of the patio is 11 ft.

Example 9

The dimensions of a triangular sail are 18 ft, 11 ft, and 15 ft. What is the perimeter of the sail?

Strategy

To find the perimeter, use the formula for the perimeter of a triangle. Substitute 18 for *a*, 11 for *b*, and 15 for *c*. Solve for *P*.

Solution

$P = a + b + c$
$P = 18 + 11 + 15$
$P = 44$

The perimeter of the sail is 44 ft.

Example 8

The infield for a softball field is a square with each side of length 60 ft. Find the perimeter of the infield.

Your Strategy

Your Solution

Example 10

What is the perimeter of a standard piece of typing paper that measures $8\frac{1}{2}$ in. by 11 in.?

Your Strategy

Your Solution

Solutions on p. A4

OBJECTIVE C   Area of a polygon

Area is the amount of surface in a region. Area can be used to describe the size of a rug, a parking lot, a farm, or a national park. Area is measured in square units.

A square that measures 1 in. on each side has an area of 1 square inch, written 1 in².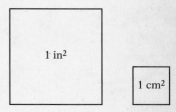

A square that measures 1 cm on each side has an area of 1 square centimeter, written 1 cm².

Larger areas can be measured in square feet (ft²), square meters (m²), square miles (mi²), acres (43,560 ft²), or any other square unit.

The area of a geometric figure is the number of squares that are necessary to cover the figure. In the figures below, two rectangles have been drawn and covered with squares. In the figure on the left, 12 squares, each of area 1 cm², were used to cover the rectangle. The area of the rectangle is 12 cm². In the figure on the right, 6 squares, each of area 1 in², were used to cover the rectangle. The area of the rectangle is 6 in².

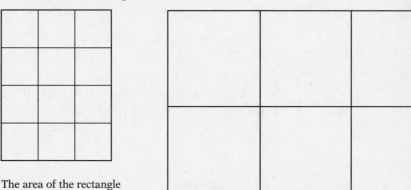

The area of the rectangle is 12 cm².

The area of the rectangle is 6 in².

Note from the above figures that the area of a rectangle can be found by multiplying the length of the rectangle by its width.

> **Area of a Rectangle**
> Let L represent the length and W the width of a rectangle.
> The area, A, of the rectangle is given by $A = LW$.

The area of the rectangle shown at the right is the length times width.

$$A = LW = 11(7) = 77$$

The area is 77 m².

7 m

11 m

Area of a Square

Let s represent the length of a side of a square.
The area, A, of the square is given by $A = s^2$.

■ The area of the square shown at the
right is the square of the length of a
side.

$$A = s^2 = 9^2 = 81$$

The area is 81 mi^2.

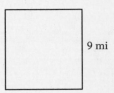

9 mi

Figure $ABCD$ is a parallelogram. BC is the
base, b, of the parallelogram. AE,
perpendicular to the base, is the **height**, h,
of the parallelogram.

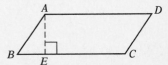

Any side of a parallelogram can be designated as the base. The corresponding
height is found by drawing a line segment perpendicular to the base from the
opposite side.

A rectangle can be formed from a parallelogram by cutting a right triangle
from one end of the parallelogram and attaching it to the other end. The area
of the resulting rectangle will equal the area of the original parallelogram.

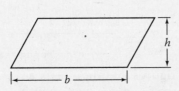

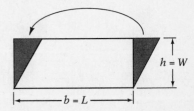

Area of a Parallelogram

Let b represent the length of the base and h the height of a parallelogram. The area, A, of the parallelogram is given by $A = bh$.

■ The area of the parallelogram shown at
the right is the base times the height.

$$A = bh = 12 \cdot 6 = 72$$

The area is 72 m^2.

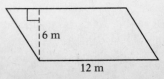

6 m

12 m

Figure *ABC* is a triangle. *AB* is the
base, *b*, of the triangle. *CD*,
perpendicular to the base, is the
height, *h*, of the triangle.

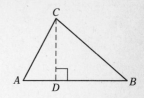

Any side of a triangle can be designated
as the base. The corresponding height is
found by drawing a line segment
perpendicular to the base from the
vertex opposite the base.

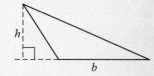

Consider the triangle with base *b* and
height *h* shown at the right. By
extending a line from *C* parallel to the
base *AB* and equal in length to the base,
a parallelogram is formed. The area of
the parallelogram is *bh* and is twice the
area of the triangle. Therefore, the area
of the triangle is one-half the area of
the parallelogram, or $\frac{1}{2}bh$.

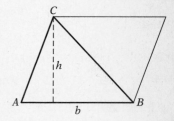

Area of a Triangle

Let *b* represent the length of the base and *h* the height of a triangle.
The area, *A*, of the triangle is given by $A = \frac{1}{2}bh$.

The area of the triangle shown at
the right is one-half the base times
the height.

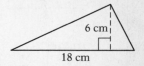

$$A = \frac{1}{2}bh = \frac{1}{2} \cdot 18 \cdot 6 = 54$$

The area is 54 cm^2.

Figure *ABCD* is a trapezoid. *AB* is one
base, b_1, of the trapezoid, and *CD* is the
other base, b_2. *AE*, perpendicular to the
two bases, is the **height**, *h*.

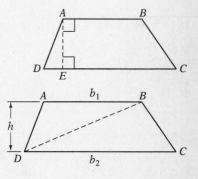

In the trapezoid at the right, the line
segment *BD* divides the trapezoid into
two triangles, *ABD* and *BCD*. In
triangle *ABD*, b_1 is the base and *h* is the
height. In triangle *BCD*, b_2 is the base
and *h* is the height. The area of the
trapezoid is the sum of the areas of the
two triangles.

Area of trapezoid *ABCD* = Area of triangle *ABD* + Area of triangle *BCD*

$$= \frac{1}{2}b_1h + \frac{1}{2}b_2h = \frac{1}{2}h(b_1 + b_2)$$

> ### Area of a Trapezoid
> Let b_1 and b_2 represent the lengths of the bases and h the height of a trapezoid. The area, A, of the trapezoid is given by $A = \frac{1}{2}h(b_1 + b_2)$.

The area of a trapezoid is one-half the product of the height and the sum of the bases.

$$A = \frac{1}{2}h(b_1 + b_2) = \frac{1}{2} \cdot 8(15 + 5) = 4(20)$$

$$= 80$$

The area of the trapezoid at the right is 80 in^2.

15 in.

8 in.

5 in.

Example 11

The Parks and Recreation Department of a city plans to plant grass seed in a playground that has the shape of a trapezoid, as shown below. Each bag of grass seed will seed 1,500 ft^2. How many bags of grass seed should the department purchase?

80 ft

64 ft

115 ft

Strategy

To find the number of bags of grass seed to be purchased:
► Use the formula for the area of a trapezoid to find the area of the playground.
► Divide the area of the playground by the area one bag will seed (1,500).

Solution

$$A = \frac{1}{2}h(b_1 + b_2)$$

$$A = \frac{1}{2} \cdot 64(80 + 115)$$

$A = 6,240$ The area of the play-
                ground is 6,240 ft^2.

$6,240 \div 1,500 = 4.16$

Because a portion of a fifth bag is needed, 5 bags of grass seed should be purchased.

Example 12

An interior designer decides to wallpaper two walls of a room. Each roll of wallpaper will cover 30 ft^2. Each wall measures 8 ft by 12 ft. How many rolls of wallpaper should be purchased?

Your Strategy

Your Solution

Solution on p. A4

2 EXERCISES

▶ **Objective A**

Which of the figures are polygons?

1.

A   B   C

2.

A   B   C

Name each polygon.

3.
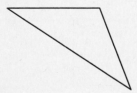

4.

5.
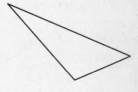

6.
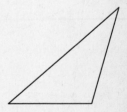

Classify each triangle as isosceles, equilateral, or scalene.

7.
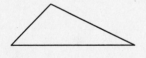

8.
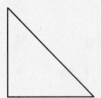

9.
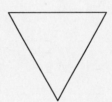

10.
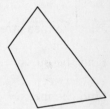

Classify each triangle as acute, obtuse, or right.

11.

12.
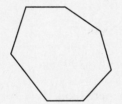

13.
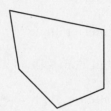

14.

Find the measure of $\angle x$.

15.
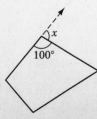

16.
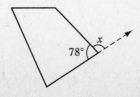

17.
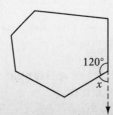

18.
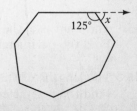

Solve.

19. In a hexagon, the measure of one of the interior angles is 84°. Find the measure of one of the corresponding exterior angles.

20. In a heptagon, the measure of one of the interior angles is 79°. Find the measure of one of the corresponding exterior angles.

21. Find the sum of the measures of the interior angles of a nonagon.

22. Find the sum of the measures of the interior angles of a heptagon.

23. Find the sum of the measures of the interior angles of a quadrilateral.

24. Find the sum of the measures of the interior angles of a hexagon.

25. Find the measure of each interior angle of a regular quadrilateral.

26. Find the measure of each interior angle of a regular octagon.

27. Find the measure of each interior angle of a regular decagon.

28. Find the measure of each interior angle of a regular pentagon.

▶ **Objective B**

Find the perimeter.

29.
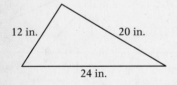
12 in.   20 in.   24 in.

30.
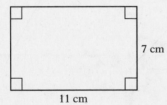
7 cm   11 cm

31.
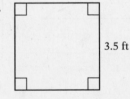
3.5 ft

32.
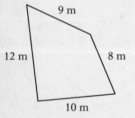
9 m   12 m   8 m   10 m

33.
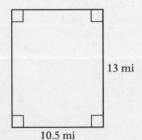
13 mi   10.5 mi

34.
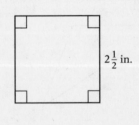
$2\frac{1}{2}$ in.

Solve.

35. The lengths of the three sides of a triangle are 3.8 cm, 5.2 cm, and 8.4 cm. Find the perimeter of the triangle.

36. The lengths of the three sides of a triangle are 7.5 m, 6.1 m, and 4.9 m. Find the perimeter of the triangle.

Solve.

37. The length of each of two sides of an isosceles triangle is $2\frac{1}{2}$ cm. The third side measures 3 cm. Find the perimeter of the triangle.

38. The length of each side of an equilateral triangle is $4\frac{1}{2}$ in. Find the perimeter of the triangle.

39. A rectangle has a length of 8.5 m and a width of 3.5 m. Find the perimeter of the rectangle.

40. Find the perimeter of a rectangle that has a length of $5\frac{1}{2}$ ft and a width of 4 ft.

41. The length of each side of a square is 12.2 cm. Find the perimeter of the square.

42. Find the perimeter of a square that is 0.5 m on each side.

43. Find the perimeter of a regular pentagon that measures 3.5 in. on each side.

44. What is the perimeter of a regular hexagon that measures 8.5 cm on each side?

45. How many feet of fencing should be purchased for a rectangular garden that is 18 ft long and 12 ft wide?

46. How many meters of binding are required to bind the edge of a rectangular quilt that measures 3.5 m by 8.5 m?

47. Wall-to-wall carpeting is installed in a room that is 12 ft long and 10 ft wide. The edges of the carpet are nailed to the floor. Along how many feet must the carpet be nailed down?

48. The length of a rectangular park is 55 yd. The width is 47 yd. How many yards of fencing are needed to surround the park?

49. The perimeter of a rectangular playground is 440 ft. If the width is 100 ft, what is the length of the playground?

50. A vegetable garden has a perimeter of 64 ft. The length of the garden is 20 ft. What is the width of the garden?

51. Each of two sides of a triangular banner measures 18 in. If the perimeter of the banner is 46 in., what is the length of the third side of the banner?

52. The perimeter of an equilateral triangle is 13.2 cm. What is the length of each side of the triangle?

53. The perimeter of a square picture frame is 48 in. Find the length of each side of the frame.

54. A square rug has a perimeter of 32 ft. Find the length of each edge of the rug.

Solve.

55. Bias binding is needed to sew around the edge of a tablecloth measuring 72 in. by 45 in. If the bias binding comes in packages containing 15 ft of binding, how many packages of bias binding are needed for the tablecloth?

56. Including the end zone, a football field is 120 yd long and $53\frac{1}{3}$ yd wide.

    You are relining the field, and must remark the side lines and end lines, as well as remark a line along the width of the field every 10 yd. How many yards of marking will you make on the field?

▶ **Objective C**

Find the area.

57.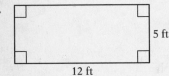

58.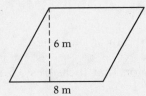

59.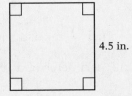

60.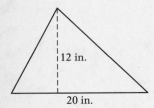

61.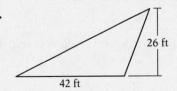

62.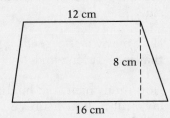

Solve.

63. The length of a side of a square is 12.5 cm. Find the area of the square.

64. Each side of a square measures $3\frac{1}{2}$ in. Find the area of the square.

65. The length of a rectangle is 38 in. and the width is 15 in. Find the area of the rectangle.

66. Find the area of a rectangle that has a length of 6.5 m and a width of 3.8 m.

67. The length of the base of a parallelogram is 16 in. and the height is 12 in. Find the area of the parallelogram.

68. The height of a parallelogram is 3.4 m and the length of the base is 5.2 m. Find the area of the parallelogram.

69. The length of the base of a triangle is 6 ft. The height is 4.5 ft. Find the area of the triangle.

Solve.

70. The height of a triangle is 4.2 cm. The length of the base is 5 cm. Find the area of the triangle.

71. The length of one base of a trapezoid is 35 cm and the length of the other base is 20 cm. If the height is 12 cm, what is the area of the trapezoid?

72. The height of a trapezoid is 5 in. The bases measure 16 in. and 18 in. Find the area of the trapezoid.

73. Find the area of a rectangular flower garden that measures 14 ft by 9 ft.

74. What is the area of a square patio that measures 8.5 m on each side?

75. Artificial turf is being used to cover a playing field. If the field is rectangular with a length of 100 yd and a width of 75 yd, how much artificial turf must be purchased to cover the field?

76. A fabric wall hanging is to fill a space that measures 5 m by 3.5 m. Allowing for 0.1 m of the fabric to be folded back along each edge, how much fabric must be purchased for the wall hanging?

77. The area of a rectangle is 300 in.^{2}. If the length of the rectangle is 30 in., what is the width?

78. The width of a rectangle is 12 ft. If the area is 312 ft^2, what is the length of the rectangle?

79. The height of a triangle is 5 m. The area of the triangle is 50 m^2. Find the length of the base of the triangle.

80. The length of the base of a triangle is 4 cm. If the area of the triangle is 20 cm^2, what is the height of the triangle?

81. The area of a parallelogram is 42 m^2. If the height of the parallelogram is 7 m, what is the length of the base?

82. The length of the base of a parallelogram is 14 cm. The area is 98 cm^2. Find the height of the parallelogram.

83. You plan to stain the wooden deck attached to your house. The deck measures 10 ft by 8 ft. If a quart of stain will cover 50 ft^2, how many quarts of stain should you purchase?

84. You want to tile your kitchen floor. The floor measures 12 ft by 9 ft. How many tiles, each a square with side $1\frac{1}{2}$ ft, should you purchase for the job?

85. Two walls of a child's room, one measuring 9 ft by 8 ft and the other measuring 11 ft by 8 ft, are being wallpapered with wallpaper that costs $18.50 per roll. Each roll of the wallpaper will cover 40 ft^2. What is the cost of the wallpaper?

Solve.

86. An urban renewal project involves reseeding a park that is in the shape of a square, 60 ft on each side. Each bag of grass seed costs $5.75 and will seed 1,200 ft². How much money should be budgeted for buying grass seed for the park?

87. You want to install wall-to-wall carpeting in your living room, which measures 15 ft by 24 ft. If the cost of the carpet you would like to purchase is $15.95 per square yard, what is the cost of the carpeting for your living room? (Hint: 9 sq ft = 1 sq yd)

88. You want to paint the walls of your bedroom. Two walls measure 15 ft by 9 ft, and the other two walls measure 12 ft by 9 ft. If the paint you wish to purchase costs $12.98 per gallon, and each gallon will cover 400 ft² of wall, how much will you spend on paint?

89. A walkway 2 m wide surrounds a rectangular plot of grass. The plot is 30 m long and 20 m wide. What is the area of the walkway?

90. Pleated draperies for a window must be twice as wide as the width of the window. Draperies are being made for four windows, each 2 ft wide and 4 ft high. Since the drapes will fall slightly below the window sill and extra fabric will be needed for hemming the drapes, 1 ft must be added to the height of the window. How much material must be purchased to make the drapes?

▶ *Supplemental Exercises*

91. Find the ratio of the areas of two squares if the ratio of the lengths of their sides is 2:3.

92. If both the length and the width of a rectangle are doubled, how many times larger is the area of the resulting rectangle?

93. A **hexagram** is a six-pointed star, formed by extending each of the sides of a regular hexagon into an equilateral triangle. A hexagram is shown at the right. Use a pencil, paper, protractor, and ruler to create a hexagram.

94. Determine whether each statement is always true, sometimes true, or never true.
    a. If two triangles have the same perimeter, then they have the same area.
    b. If two rectangles have the same area, then they have the same perimeter.
    c. If two squares have the same area, then the sides of the squares have the same length.
    d. An equilateral triangle is also an isosceles triangle.

95. Prepare a report on the history of quilts in America. Find examples of quilt patterns that incorporate regular polygons. Use pieces of cardboard to create the shapes needed for one block of one of the quilt patterns you learned about.

96. The **apothem** of a regular polygon is the distance from the center of the polygon to a side. Explain how to derive a formula for the area of a regular polygon using the apothem. (*Hint:* Use the formula for the area of a triangle.)

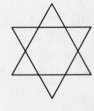

apothem

SECTION **3** **Triangles**

OBJECTIVE **A** **Right triangles**

A **right triangle** contains one right angle. The side opposite the right angle is called the **hypotenuse**. The other two sides are called **legs**.

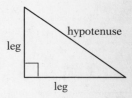

The angles in a right triangle are usually labeled with the capital letters *A*, *B*, and *C*, with *C* reserved for the right angle. The side opposite angle *A* is side *a*, the side opposite angle *B* is side *b*, and *c* is the hypotenuse.

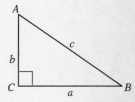

The Greek mathematician Pythagoras is generally credited with the discovery that the square of the hypotenuse of a right triangle is equal to the sum of the squares of the two legs. This is called the **Pythagorean Theorem**. However, the Babylonians used this theorem more than 1,000 years before Pythagoras lived.

In the figure at the right is a right triangle with legs measuring 3 units and 4 units and a hypotenuse measuring 5 units. Each side of the triangle is also the side of a square. The number of square units in the area of the largest square is equal to the sum of the areas of the smaller squares.

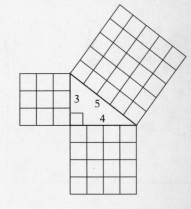

$$\text{Square of the hypotenuse} = \text{sum of the squares of the two legs}$$

$$5^2 = 3^2 + 4^2$$
$$25 = 9 + 16$$
$$25 = 25$$

Pythagorean Theorem

If *a* and *b* are the lengths of the legs of a right triangle and *c* is the length of the hypotenuse, then $c^2 = a^2 + b^2$.

If the lengths of two sides of a right triangle are known, the Pythagorean Theorem can be used to find the length of the third side.

Consider a right triangle with legs that measure 5 cm and 12 cm. Use the Pythagorean Theorem, with $a = 5$ and $b = 12$, to find the length of the hypotenuse.

$$c^2 = a^2 + b^2$$
$$c^2 = 5^2 + 12^2$$
$$c^2 = 25 + 144$$
$$c^2 = 169$$

This equation states that the square of c is 169. Since $13^2 = 169$, $c = 13$, and the length of the hypotenuse is 13 cm. We can find c by taking the square root of 169: $\sqrt{169} = 13$. This suggests the following property.

Square Root Property

If $r^2 = s$, then $r = \sqrt{s}$ or $r = -\sqrt{s}$, and r is called the square root of s.

Since we are interested in distance, and distance is never negative, we consider only the positive square root $\sqrt{s}$ and not the negative square root $-\sqrt{s}$.

The Square Root Property and its application can be illustrated as follows:

Because $5^2 = 25$, $5 = \sqrt{25}$. Therefore, if $c^2 = 25$, $c = \sqrt{25} = 5$.

Because $7^2 = 49$, $7 = \sqrt{49}$. Therefore, if $a^2 = 49$, $a = \sqrt{49} = 7$.

Recall that numbers whose square roots are integers, such as 25 and 49, are perfect squares. If a number is not a perfect square, a calculator can be used to find an approximate square root when a decimal approximation is required. For example, $\sqrt{35} \approx 5.916$ and $\sqrt{93} \approx 9.644$.

The length of one leg of a right triangle is 8 in. The hypotenuse is 12 in. Find the length of the other leg. Round to the nearest hundredth.

Use the Pythagorean Theorem. $a^2 + b^2 = c^2$
$a = 8, c = 12$ $8^2 + b^2 = 12^2$
Solve for b^2. $64 + b^2 = 144$
                                    $b^2 = 80$

Use the Square Root Property.
Since $b^2 = 80$, b is the square root of 80. $b = \sqrt{80}$

Use a calculator to approximate $\sqrt{80}$. $b \approx 8.94$

The length of the other leg is approximately 8.94 in.

The Pythagorean Theorem can be used to find a relationship among the sides of two special right triangles, the 45°–45°–90° triangle and the 30°–60°–90° triangle. These two cases are considered below.

Recall that an isosceles triangle has two equal angles. In an **isosceles right triangle**, $\angle A$ and $\angle B$ both measure 45°. For this reason, an isosceles right triangle is also called a **45°–45°–90° triangle.**

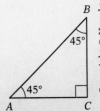

Find the hypotenuse of an isosceles right triangle if the length of one of the legs measures 1 unit.

Use the Pythagorean Theorem.
In an isosceles right triangle,
both legs are of equal length.
$a = 1, b = 1$

$c^2 = a^2 + b^2$
$c^2 = 1^2 + 1^2$
$c^2 = 1 + 1$
$c^2 = 2$

Use the Square Root Property.

$c = \sqrt{2}$

The hypotenuse is $\sqrt{2}$ units.

Properties of an Isosceles Right Triangle

In an isosceles right triangle, the measure of each of the two equal angles is 45°. The length of the hypotenuse is $\sqrt{2}$ times the length of one of the legs.

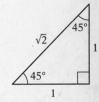

Determine the length of the hypotenuse of an isosceles right triangle if each leg measures 7 m. Round to the nearest tenth.

For an isosceles right triangle, the length of the hypotenuse is $\sqrt{2}$ times the length of a leg.

$c = \sqrt{2}$ (length of a leg)
$c = \sqrt{2}(7)$

$\sqrt{2}(7)$ is the exact length.

Use a calculator to approximate $\sqrt{2}(7)$.

$c \approx 9.9$

The length of the hypotenuse is approximately 9.9 m.

The second special right triangle is the **30°–60°–90° triangle.** The acute angles in a 30°–60°–90° triangle measure 30° and 60°.

If two 30°–60°–90° triangles, each with a hypotenuse of 2 units, are positioned so that the longer legs of each triangle lie on the same line segment, then an equilateral triangle is formed and the shorter leg of each triangle is 1 unit.

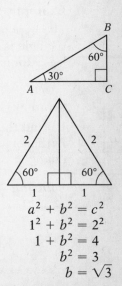

Use the Pythagorean Theorem to find the length of the longer leg. $a = 1, c = 2$

$a^2 + b^2 = c^2$
$1^2 + b^2 = 2^2$
$1 + b^2 = 4$
$b^2 = 3$

Use the Square Root Property.

$b = \sqrt{3}$

The length of the longer leg is $\sqrt{3}$ units.

Properties of a 30°–60°–90° Triangle

In a 30°–60°–90° triangle, the shorter leg is opposite the 30° angle. The length of the hypotenuse, c, is 2 times the length of the shorter leg. The length of the longer leg is $\sqrt{3}$ times the length of the shorter leg.

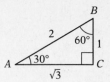

Determine the length of the hypotenuse of a 30°–60°–90° triangle if the shorter leg is 3 ft.

For a 30°–60°–90° triangle, the length of the hypotenuse is 2 times the length of the shorter leg.

$c = 2(\text{length of the shorter leg})$
$c = 2(3)$
$c = 6$

The length of the hypotenuse is 6 ft.

Example 1

The two legs of a right triangle measure 12 ft and 9 ft. Find the hypotenuse of the right triangle.

Strategy

To find the hypotenuse, use the Pythagorean Theorem. $a = 12$, $b = 9$.

Solution

$c^2 = a^2 + b^2$
$c^2 = 12^2 + 9^2 = 144 + 81 = 225$
$c = \sqrt{225} = 15$

The length of the hypotenuse is 15 ft.

Example 2

The hypotenuse of a right triangle measures 3.2 m, and one leg measures 2.6 m. Find the measure of the other leg. Round to the nearest hundredth.

Your Strategy

Your Solution

Example 3

The hypotenuse of an isosceles right triangle is 10 cm. Find the length of the legs. Round to the nearest hundredth.

Strategy

To find the length of the legs, use the Pythagorean Theorem. For an isosceles triangle, $a = b$.

Solution

$a^2 + b^2 = c^2$
$a^2 + a^2 = 10^2$
$2a^2 = 100$
$a^2 = 50$
$a = \sqrt{50} \approx 7.07$

The length of each leg is 7.07 cm.

Example 4

The side opposite the 30° angle in a 30°–60°–90° triangle is 4 in. Find the exact measures of the other two sides of the triangle.

Your Strategy

Your Solution

Solutions on p. A5

Example 5

The lengths of the legs in a 30°–60°–90° triangle are 6 m and $6\sqrt{3}$ m. Find the perimeter of the triangle. Round to the nearest tenth.

Strategy

To find the perimeter of the triangle:
▶ Use the relationships between the sides of a 30°–60°–90° triangle to find the length of the hypotenuse.
▶ Use the formula for the perimeter of a triangle.

Solution

$c = 2$(length of the shorter leg)
$c = 2(6)$
$c = 12$ The hypotenuse is 12 m.

$P = a + b + c$
$P = 6 + 6\sqrt{3} + 12$
$P = 18 + 6\sqrt{3} \approx 28.4$

The perimeter of the triangle is 28.4 m.

Example 6

The length of a leg in an isosceles right triangle is 4 cm. Find the perimeter of the triangle. Round to the nearest tenth.

Your Strategy

Your Solution

Example 7

Find the area of triangle *ABC*.

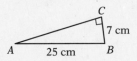

Strategy

To find the area of the triangle:
▶ Use the Pythagorean Theorem to find the length of side *AC*.
▶ Use the formula for the area of a triangle. Let side *AC* be the base and side *BC* be the height.

Solution

$a^2 + b^2 = c^2$
$7^2 + b^2 = 25^2$
$49 + b^2 = 625$
$b^2 = 576$
$b = \sqrt{576}$
$b = 24$ The length of side *AC* is 24 cm.

$A = \dfrac{1}{2}bh = \dfrac{1}{2}(24)(7) = 84$

The area of the triangle is 84 cm².

Example 8

Find the area of triangle *ABC*. Round to the nearest tenth.

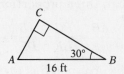

Your Strategy

Your Solution

Solutions on p. A5

OBJECTIVE **B**   **Similar triangles**

Similar objects have the same shape but not necessarily the same size. A tennis ball is similar to a basketball. A model ship is similar to an actual ship.

Similar objects have corresponding parts; for example, the rudder on the model ship corresponds to the rudder on the actual ship. The relationship between the sizes of each of the corresponding parts can be written as a ratio, and each ratio will be the same. If the rudder on the model ship is $\frac{1}{100}$ the size of the rudder on the actual ship, then the model wheelhouse is $\frac{1}{100}$ the size of the actual wheelhouse, the width of the model is $\frac{1}{100}$ of the width of the actual ship, and so on.

The two triangles *ABC* and *DEF* are similar. Side *AB* corresponds to side *DE*, side *BC* corresponds to side *EF*, and side *AC* corresponds to side *DF*. The ratios of corresponding sides are equal.

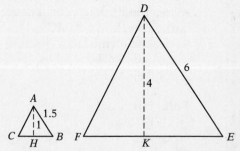

$$\frac{AB}{DE} = \frac{2}{6} = \frac{1}{3}, \quad \frac{BC}{EF} = \frac{3}{9} = \frac{1}{3}, \quad \text{and}$$

$$\frac{AC}{DF} = \frac{4}{12} = \frac{1}{3}.$$

Since the ratios of corresponding sides are equal, three proportions can be formed.

$$\frac{AB}{DE} = \frac{BC}{EF}, \quad \frac{AB}{DE} = \frac{AC}{DF}, \quad \text{and} \quad \frac{BC}{EF} = \frac{AC}{DF}.$$

The corresponding angles in similar triangles are equal. Therefore,

$$\angle A = \angle D, \quad \angle B = \angle E, \quad \text{and} \quad \angle C = \angle F.$$

Triangles *ABC* and *DEF* at the right are similar triangles. *AH* and *DK* are the heights of the triangles. The ratio of heights of similar triangles equals the ratio of corresponding sides.

Ratio of heights $= \dfrac{1}{4}$

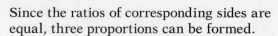

Ratio of corresponding sides $= \dfrac{1.5}{6} = \dfrac{1}{4}$

> ### *Properties of Similar Triangles*
>
> For similar triangles, corresponding angles are equal, and the ratios of corresponding sides are equal. The ratio of corresponding heights is equal to the ratio of corresponding sides.

The two triangles at the right are similar triangles. Find the length of side *EF*. Round to the nearest tenth.

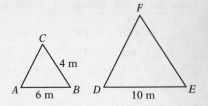

The triangles are similar, so the ratios of corresponding sides are equal.

$$\frac{EF}{BC} = \frac{DE}{AB}$$

$$\frac{EF}{4} = \frac{10}{6}$$

$$6(EF) = 4(10)$$
$$6(EF) = 40$$
$$EF \approx 6.7$$

The length of side *EF* is 6.7 m.

Example 9

Triangles *ABC* and *DEF* are similar. Find *FG*, the height of triangle *DEF*.

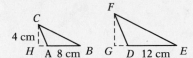

Strategy

To find *FG*, write a proportion using the fact that, in similar triangles, the ratio of corresponding sides equals the ratio of corresponding heights. Solve the proportion for *FG*.

Solution

$$\frac{AB}{DE} = \frac{CH}{FG}$$

$$\frac{8}{12} = \frac{4}{FG}$$

$$8(FG) = 12(4)$$
$$8(FG) = 48$$
$$FG = 6$$

The height *FG* of triangle *DEF* is 6 cm.

Example 10

Triangles *ABC* and *DEF* are similar. Find *FG*, the height of triangle *DEF*.

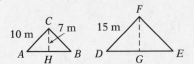

Your Strategy

Your Solution

Solution on p. A5

Example 11

Triangles *ABC* and *DEF* are similar. Find the area of triangle *DEF*.

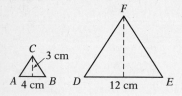

Strategy

To find the area of triangle *DEF*:
▶ Solve a proportion to find the height of triangle *DEF*. Let h_1 represent the height of triangle *ABC* and h_2 represent the height of triangle *DEF*.
▶ Use the formula for the area of a triangle.

Solution

$$\frac{AB}{DE} = \frac{h_1}{h_2}$$

$$\frac{4}{12} = \frac{3}{h_2}$$

$$4 \cdot h_2 = 12 \cdot 3$$
$$4h_2 = 36$$
$$h_2 = 9 \qquad \text{The height of triangle } DEF \text{ is 9 cm.}$$

$$A = \frac{1}{2}bh = \frac{1}{2}(12)(9) = 54$$

The area of triangle *DEF* is 54 cm².

Example 12

Triangles *ABC* and *DEF* are similar. Find the perimeter of triangle *ABC*.

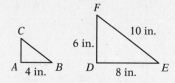

Your Strategy

Your Solution

Solution on p. A5

OBJECTIVE C   Congruent triangles

Congruent objects have the same shape *and* the same size.

The two triangles at the right are congruent. They have exactly the same size.

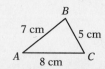
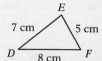

Congruent and similar triangles differ in that congruent means that the corresponding sides and angles of the triangle must be equal; for similar triangles, corresponding angles are equal, but corresponding sides are not necessarily the same length.

The three major rules used to determine if two triangles are congruent are given below.

Side-Side-Side Rule (SSS)

Two triangles are congruent if the three sides of one triangle equal the corresponding three sides of a second triangle.

In the triangles at the right, $AC = DE$, $AB = EF$, and $BC = DF$. The corresponding sides of triangles ABC and DEF are equal. The triangles are congruent by the SSS Rule.

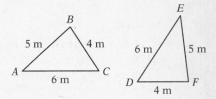

Side-Angle-Side Rule (SAS)

If two sides and the included angle of one triangle equal two sides and the included angle of a second triangle, the two triangles are congruent.

In the two triangles at the right, $AB = EF$, $AC = DE$, and $\angle BAC = \angle DEF$. The triangles are congruent by the SAS Rule.

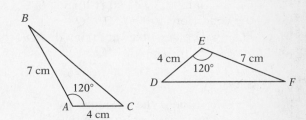

Angle-Side-Angle Rule (ASA)

If two angles and the included side of one triangle equal the two angles and the included side of a second triangle, the two triangles are congruent.

For triangles ABC and DEF at the right, $\angle A = \angle F$, $\angle C = \angle E$, and $AC = EF$. The triangles are congruent by the ASA Rule.

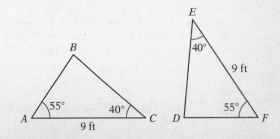

Example 13

In the figure below, is triangle *ABC* congruent to triangle *DEF*?

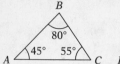

Strategy

To determine if the triangles are congruent, determine if one of the rules for congruence is satisfied.

Solution

The triangles do not satisfy the SSS Rule, the SAS Rule, or the ASA Rule. The triangles are not necessarily congruent.

Note: If corresponding angles of a triangle are equal, the triangles are similar but not necessarily congruent.

Example 14

In the figure below, is triangle *PQR* congruent to triangle *MNO*?

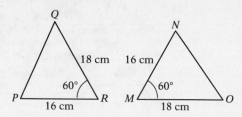

Your Strategy

Your Solution

Example 15

Given triangle *PQR* and triangle *MNO*, do the conditions ∠*P* = ∠*O*, ∠*Q* = ∠*M*, and *PQ* = *MO* guarantee that triangle *PQR* is congruent to triangle *MNO*?

Strategy

To determine if the triangles are congruent, draw a sketch of the two triangles and determine if one of the rules for congruence is satisfied.

Solution

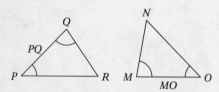

Because two angles and the included side of one triangle equal two angles and the included side of a second triangle, the triangles are congruent by the ASA Rule.

Example 16

Given triangle *ABC* and triangle *DEF*, do the conditions ∠*A* = ∠*D*, ∠*C* = ∠*F*, and *AB* = *EF* guarantee that triangle *ABC* is congruent to triangle *DEF*?

Your Strategy

Your Solution

Solutions on p. A6

3 EXERCISES

▶ **Objective A**

Find the unknown side of each triangle. Round to the nearest tenth.

1.

3 in.
4 in.

2.
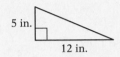
5 in.
12 in.

3.

5 cm
7 cm

4.

7 cm
9 cm

5.

15 ft
10 ft

6.
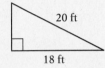
20 ft
18 ft

7.

4 cm   6 cm

8.

9 m   12 m

9.

9 yd
9 yd

Find the exact lengths of the two legs.

10.

20 cm
30°

11.

12 ft
30°

12.

16 cm
30°

Find the exact length of the hypotenuse of each right triangle.

13.

15 cm
45°
15 cm

14.
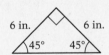
6 in.   6 in.
45°   45°

15.
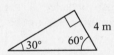
4 m
30°   60°

16.
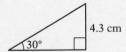
4.3 cm
30°

17.

45°
8 yd

18.
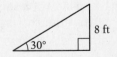
8 ft
30°

Find the area of each triangle *ABC*. Round to the nearest tenth.

19.

B
12 cm
A   C
9 cm

20.
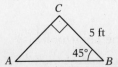
C
5 ft
A   45°   B

21.
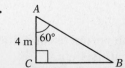
A
4 m   60°
C   B

Solve. Round to the nearest tenth.

22.   A ladder 8 m long is leaning against a building. How high on the building will the ladder reach when the bottom of the ladder is 3 m from the building?

8 m

3 m

23.   Find the distance between the centers of the holes in the metal plate.

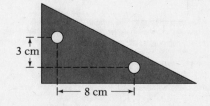

3 cm

8 cm

24.   Find the perimeter of a right triangle with legs that measure 5 cm and 9 cm.

25.   Find the perimeter of a right triangle with legs that measure 6 in. and 8 in.

26.   The lengths of the legs of a 30°–60°–90° triangle measure 8 m and $8\sqrt{3}$ m. Find the perimeter of the triangle.

27.   The lengths of the legs of a 30°–60°–90° triangle measure 3 ft and $3\sqrt{3}$ ft. Find the perimeter of the triangle.

28.   The length of a leg of an isosceles right triangle is 3 cm. Find the perimeter of the triangle.

29.   The length of a leg of an isosceles right triangle is 5 in. Find the perimeter of the triangle.

30.   The length of a side of a square is 8 m. Find the length of a diagonal of the square.

31.   The length of a side of a square is 6 in. Find the length of a diagonal of the square.

32.   Find the perimeter of rectangle *ABCD* if the length of diagonal *AC* is 6 m.

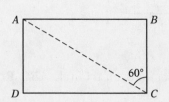

33.   Find the perimeter of rectangle *ABCD* if the length of diagonal *AC* is 4 cm.

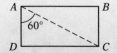

▶ **Objective B**

Find the ratio of corresponding sides for the similar triangles.

34.
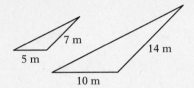

35.
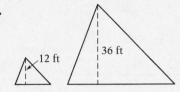

36.
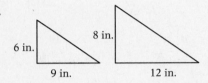

37.
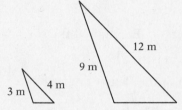

Triangles *ABC* and *DEF* are similar triangles. Solve. Round to the nearest tenth.

38. Find side *DE*.
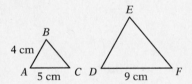

39. Find side *DE*.
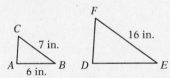

40. Find the height of triangle *DEF*.
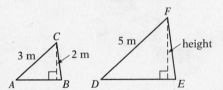

41. Find the height of triangle *ABC*.
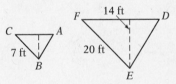

42. Find the perimeter of triangle *ABC*.
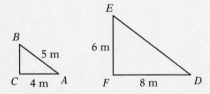

43. Find the perimeter of triangle *DEF*.
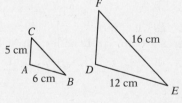

44. Find the perimeter of triangle *ABC*.
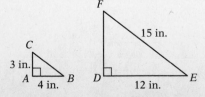

45. Find the area of triangle *DEF*.
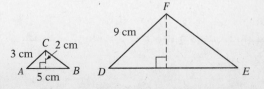

Triangles *ABC* and *DEF* are similar triangles. Solve.

46. Find the area of triangle *ABC*.

47. Find the area of triangle *DEF*.

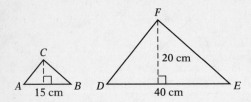

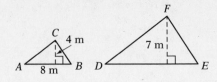

The sun's rays, objects on Earth, and the shadows cast by them form similar triangles. Solve.

48. Find the height of the flagpole.

49. Find the height of the flagpole.

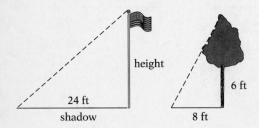

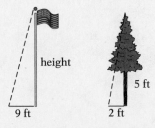

50. Find the height of the building.

51. Find the height of the building.

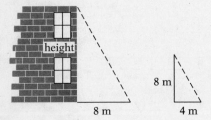

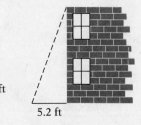

Solve.

52. Given *BD* ∥ *AE*, *BD* measures 5 cm, *AE* measures 8 cm, and *AC* measures 10 cm, find the length of *BC*.

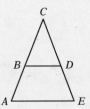

53. Given *AC* ∥ *DE*, *BD* measures 8 m, *AD* measures 12 m, and *BE* measures 6 m, find the length of *BC*.

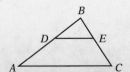

Solve.

54. Given *DE* ∥ *AC*, *DE* measures 6 in., *AC* measures 10 in., and *AB* measures 15 in., find the length of *DA*.

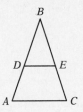

55. Given *AE* ∥ *BD*, *AB* measures 3 ft, *ED* measures 4 ft, and *BC* measures 3 ft, find the length of *CE*.

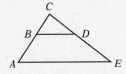

56. Given *MP* and *NQ* intersect at *O*, *NO* measures 24 cm, *MN* measures 10 cm, and the length of *MO* is twice the length of *OP*, find the perimeter of triangle *OPQ*.

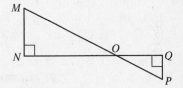

57. Given *MP* and *NQ* intersect at *O*, *NO* measures 12 m, *MN* measures 9 m, and the length of *MO* is three times the length of *OP*, find the perimeter of triangle *OPQ*.

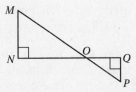

▶ **Objective C**

Determine whether or not the two triangles are congruent. If they are congruent, state by what rule they are congruent.

58.

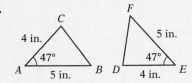

59.

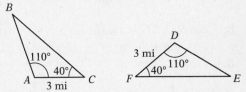

60.

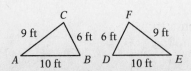

61.

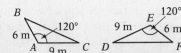

Determine whether or not the two triangles are congruent. If they are congruent, state by what rule they are congruent.

62.

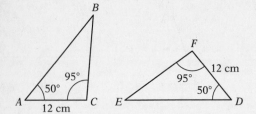

63.

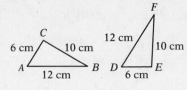

Solve.

64. Given triangle *ABC* and triangle *DEF*, do the conditions $\angle C = \angle E$, $AC = EF$, and $BC = DE$ guarantee that triangle *ABC* is congruent to triangle *DEF*? If they are congruent, by what rule are they congruent?

65. Given triangle *PQR* and triangle *MNO*, do the conditions $PR = NO$, $PQ = MO$, and $QR = MN$ guarantee that triangle *PQR* is congruent to triangle *MNO*? If they are congruent, by what rule are they congruent?

66. Given triangle *LMN* and triangle *QRS*, do the conditions $\angle M = \angle S$, $\angle N = \angle Q$, and $\angle L = \angle R$ guarantee that triangle *LMN* is congruent to triangle *QRS*? If they are congruent, by what rule are they congruent?

67. Given triangle *DEF* and triangle *JKL*, do the conditions $\angle D = \angle K$, $\angle E = \angle L$, and $DE = KL$ guarantee that triangle *DEF* is congruent to triangle *JKL*? If they are congruent, by what rule are they congruent?

68. Given triangle *ABC* and triangle *PQR*, do the conditions $\angle B = \angle P$, $BC = PQ$, and $AC = QR$ guarantee that triangle *ABC* is congruent to triangle *PQR*? If they are congruent, by what rule are they congruent?

▶ *Supplemental Exercises*

69. Congruent triangles were a topic of this section. Use the concept of congruent triangles to derive the formula for the area of a parallelogram given that the area of a rectangle is $A = LW$.

70. Determine whether each statement is always true, sometimes true, or never true.
   a. If two angles of one triangle are equal to two angles of a second triangle, then the triangles are similar triangles.
   b. Two isosceles triangles are similar triangles.
   c. Two equilateral triangles are similar triangles.
   d. Two isosceles right triangles are similar triangles.

71. Solve the Pythagorean Theorem for *c*.

w **72.** The formula for the area of an equilateral triangle is $A = \dfrac{s^2\sqrt{3}}{4}$, where *s* is a length of a side. Explain how this formula is derived. (*Hint:* Use the relationships between the sides of a 30°–60°–90° triangle and the formula for the area of a triangle.) Use the formula to find the area of an equilateral triangle that has sides measuring 8 cm.

SECTION **4** Circles

OBJECTIVE **A** Circumference and area of a circle

A **circle** is a plane figure in which all points are the same distance from point O, called the **center** of the circle.

The **diameter** of a circle is a line segment across the circle through point O. AB is a diameter of the circle at the right. The variable d is used to designate the diameter of a circle.

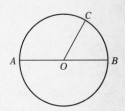

The **radius** of a circle is a line segment from the center of the circle to a point on the circle. OC is a radius of the circle at the right. The variable r is used to designate the radius of a circle.

The length of the diameter is twice the length of the radius.

$$d = 2r \quad \text{or} \quad r = \frac{1}{2}d$$

The distance around a circle is called the **circumference**. The formula for the circumference, C, of a circle is:

$$C = \pi d$$

Because $d = 2r$, the formula for the circumference can be written:

$$C = 2\pi r$$

The formula for circumference uses the number π (pi), which is an irrational number. The value of π can be approximated by a fraction or by a decimal.

$$\pi \approx \frac{22}{7} \quad \text{or} \quad \pi \approx 3.14$$

The π key on a scientific calculator gives a closer approximation of π than 3.14. A scientific calculator is used in this chapter to find approximate values in calculations involving π.

> Find the circumference of a circle with a diameter of 6 in.

> The diameter of the circle is given. Use the circumference formula that involves the diameter. $d = 6$.

$$C = \pi d$$
$$C = \pi(6)$$

> The exact circumference of the circle is 6π in.

$$C = 6\pi$$

> An approximate measure is found by using the π key on a calculator.

$$C \approx 18.85$$

> The approximate circumference is 18.85 in.

The area of a circle is the product of π and the square of the radius.

The formula for the area, A, of a circle of radius r is $A = \pi r^2$.

$$A = \pi r^2$$

▮ Find the area of a circle that has a radius of 6 cm.

Use the formula for the area of a circle. $r = 6$.	$A = \pi r^2$
	$A = \pi(6)^2$
	$A = \pi(36)$
The exact area of the circle is 36π cm^2. An approximate measure is found by using the π key on a calculator.	$A = 36\pi$
	$A \approx 113.10$

The approximate area of the circle is 113.10 cm^2.

The formulas for the circumference and area of a circle are summarized below.

The Circumference and Area of a Circle

The circumference, C, of a circle with diameter d and radius r is given by $C = \pi d$ or $C = 2\pi r$.

The area, A, of a circle with radius r is given by $A = \pi r^2$.

Example 1

Find the circumference of a circle with a radius of 15 cm. Round to the nearest hundredth.

Strategy

To find the circumference, use the circumference formula that involves the radius. An approximation is asked for; use the π key on a calculator. $r = 15$.

Solution

$C = 2\pi r = 2\pi(15) = 30\pi \approx 94.25$

The circumference is 94.25 cm.

Example 3

Find the area of a circle with a diameter of 5 ft. Give the exact measure.

Strategy

To find the area:
▶ Find the radius of the circle.
▶ Use the formula for the area of a circle. Leave the answer in terms of π.

Solution

$r = \dfrac{1}{2}d = \dfrac{1}{2}(5) = 2.5$

$A = \pi r^2 = \pi(2.5)^2 = \pi(6.25) = 6.25\pi$

The area of the circle is 6.25π ft^2.

Example 2

Find the circumference of a circle with a diameter of 9 in. Give the exact measure.

Your Strategy

Your Solution

Example 4

Find the area of a circle with a radius of 11 cm. Round to the nearest hundredth.

Your Strategy

Your Solution

Solutions on p. A6

4 EXERCISES

▶ **Objective A**

Find the circumference and area of each figure. Give both the exact value and an approximation to the nearest hundredth.

1.
4 cm

2.
12 m

3.
5.5 mi

4.
18 in.

5.
17 ft

6.
6.6 km

Solve.

7. The radius of a circle is 4.2 cm. Find the length of a diameter of the circle.

8. The diameter of a circle is 0.56 m. Find the length of a radius of the circle.

9. Find the circumference of a circle that has a diameter of 1.5 in. Give the exact value.

10. The diameter of a circle is 4.2 ft. Find the circumference of the circle. Round to the nearest hundredth.

11. The radius of a circle is 36 cm. Find the circumference of the circle. Round to the nearest hundredth.

12. Find the circumference of a circle that has a radius of 2.5 m. Give the exact value.

13. The radius of a circle is 5 in. Find the area of the circle. Give the exact value.

14. Find the area of a circle with a radius of 14 m. Round to the nearest hundredth.

15. Find the area of a circle that has a diameter of 3.4 ft. Round to the nearest hundredth.

16. The diameter of a circle is 6.5 m. Find the area of the circle. Give the exact value.

17. The circumference of a circle is 8 cm. Find the length of a diameter of the circle. Round to the nearest hundredth.

18. The circumference of a circle is 15 in. Find the length of a radius of the circle. Round to the nearest hundredth.

Solve.

19. Find the length of molding needed to put around a circular table that is 4.2 ft in diameter. Round to the nearest hundredth.

20. How much binding is needed to bind the edge of a circular rug that is 3 m in diameter? Round to the nearest hundredth.

21. A bicycle tire has a diameter of 24 in. How many feet does the bicycle travel when the wheel makes eight revolutions? Round to the nearest hundredth.

22. A tricycle tire has a diameter of 12 in. How many feet does the tricycle travel when the wheel makes twelve revolutions? Round to the nearest hundredth.

23. The distance from the surface of the earth to its center is 6,356 km. What is the circumference of the earth? Round to the nearest hundredth.

24. The telescope lens located on Mt. Palomar has a diameter of 200 in. Find the area of the lens. Give the exact value.

25. An irrigation system waters a circular field that has a 50-foot radius. Find the area watered by the irrigation system. Give the exact value.

26. A circle has a radius of 8 in. Find the increase in area when the radius is increased by 2 in. Round to the nearest hundredth.

27. A circle has a radius of 6 cm. Find the increase in area when the radius is doubled. Round to the nearest hundredth.

28. A circle has a diameter of 4 ft. Find the increase in area when the diameter is doubled. Round to the nearest hundredth.

▶ *Supplemental Exercises*

29. Derive a formula for the area of a circle in terms of the diameter of the circle.

30. Determine whether each statement is true or false.
    a. All radii (plural of radius) of a circle are equal.
    b. All diameters of a circle are equal.
    c. All circles are congruent.

[w] 31. Suppose a circle is cut into 16 equal pieces, which are then arranged as shown at the right. The figure formed resembles a parallelogram. What variable expression could describe the base of the parallelogram? What variable could describe its height? Explain how the formula for the area of a circle is derived from this approach.

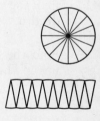

32. If the formula $C = \pi d$ is solved for π, the resulting equation is $\pi = \dfrac{C}{d}$. Therefore, π is the ratio of the circumference of a circle to the length of its diameter. Use several circular objects, such as coins, plates, tin cans, and wheels, to show that the ratio of the circumference of each object to its diameter is approximately equal to 3.14.

SECTION 5 Solids

OBJECTIVE **A**   Volume of a solid

Geometric solids are figures in space. Five common geometric solids are the rectangular solid, the sphere, the cylinder, the cone, and the pyramid.

A **rectangular solid** is one in which all six sides, called **faces**, are rectangles. The variable *L* is used to represent the length of a rectangular solid, *W* its width, and *H* its height.

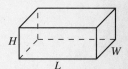

A **sphere** is a solid in which all points are the same distance from point *O*, called the **center** of the sphere. The **diameter**, *d*, of a sphere is a line across the sphere going through point *O*. The **radius**, *r*, is a line from the center to a point on the sphere. *AB* is a diameter and *OC* is a radius of the sphere shown at the right.

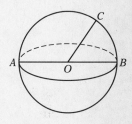

$$d = 2r \quad \text{or} \quad r = \frac{1}{2}d$$

The most common cylinder, called a **right circular cylinder,** is one in which the bases are circles and are perpendicular to the height of the cylinder. The variable *r* is used to represent the radius of the base of a cylinder, and *h* represents the height. In this text, only right circular cylinders are discussed.

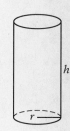

A **right circular cone** is obtained when one base of a right circular cylinder is shrunk to a point, called the **vertex**, *V*. The variable *r* is used to represent the radius of the base of the cone, and *h* represents the height. The variable *l* is used to represent the **slant height,** which is the distance from a point on the circumference of the base to the vertex. In this text, only right circular cones are discussed.

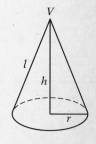

The base of a **regular pyramid** is a regular polygon, and the sides are congruent isosceles triangles. The height, *h*, is the distance from the vertex, *V*, to the base and is perpendicular to the base. The variable *l* is used to represent the **slant height,** which is the height of one of the isosceles triangles on the face of the pyramid. The regular square pyramid at the right has a square base. This is the only type of pyramid discussed in this text.

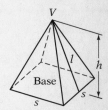

A **cube** is a special type of rectangular solid. Each of the six faces of a cube is a square. The variable s is used to represent the length of one side of a cube.

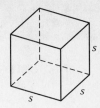

Volume is a measure of the amount of space inside a figure in space. Volume can be used to describe the amount of heating gas used for cooking, the amount of concrete delivered for the foundation of a house, or the amount of water in storage for a city's water supply.

A cube that is 1 ft on each side has a volume of 1 cubic foot, which is written 1 ft^3. A cube that measures 1 cm on each side has a volume of 1 cubic centimeter, written 1 cm^3.

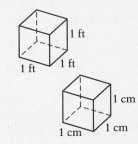

The volume of a solid is the number of cubes that are necessary to exactly fill the solid. The volume of the rectangular solid at the right is 24 cm^3 because it will hold exactly 24 cubes, each 1 cm on a side. Note that the volume can be found by multiplying the length times the width times the height.

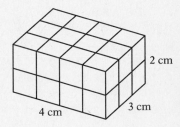

The formulas for the volumes of the geometric solids described above are given below.

Volumes of Geometric Solids

The volume, V, of a **rectangular solid** with length L, width W, and height H is given by $V = LWH$.

The volume, V, of a **cube** with side s is given by $V = s^3$.

The volume, V, of a **sphere** with radius r is given by $V = \dfrac{4}{3}\pi r^3$.

The volume, V, of a **right circular cylinder** is given by $V = \pi r^2 h$, where r is the radius of the base and h is the height.

The volume, V, of a **right circular cone** is given by $V = \dfrac{1}{3}\pi r^2 h$, where r is the radius of the circular base and h is the height.

The volume, V, of a **regular square pyramid** is given by $V = \dfrac{1}{3}s^2 h$, where s is the length of a side of the base and h is the height.

■ Find the volume of a sphere with a diameter of 6 in.

First find the radius of the sphere. $r = \dfrac{1}{2}d = \dfrac{1}{2}(6) = 3$

Use the formula for the volume of a sphere. $V = \dfrac{4}{3}\pi r^3$

$$V = \dfrac{4}{3}\pi(3)^3$$

$$V = \dfrac{4}{3}\pi(27)$$

The exact volume of the sphere is 36π in^3. $V = 36\pi$
An approximate measure can be found by
using the π key on a calculator. $V \approx 113.10$

The approximate volume is 113.10 in^3.

Example 1

The length of a rectangular solid is 5 m, the width is 3.2 m, and the height is 4 m. Find the volume of the solid.

Strategy

To find the volume, use the formula for the volume of a rectangular solid. $L = 5$, $W = 3.2$, $H = 4$.

Solution

$V = LWH = 5(3.2)(4) = 64$

The volume of the rectangular solid is 64 m^3.

Example 2

Find the volume of a cube that measures 2.5 m on a side.

Your Strategy

Your Solution

Example 3

The radius of the base of a cone is 8 cm. The height is 12 cm. Find the volume of the cone. Round to the nearest hundredth.

Strategy

To find the volume, use the formula for the volume of a cone. An approximation is asked for; use the π key on a calculator. $r = 8$, $h = 12$.

Solution

$$V = \dfrac{1}{3}\pi r^2 h$$

$$V = \dfrac{1}{3}\pi(8)^2(12) = 256\pi \approx 804.25$$

The volume of the cone is 804.25 cm^3.

Example 4

The diameter of the base of a cylinder is 8 ft. The height of the cylinder is 22 ft. Find the exact volume of the cylinder.

Your Strategy

Your Solution

Solutions on p. A6

OBJECTIVE B   Surface area of a solid

The **surface area** of a solid is the total area on the surface of the solid.

When a rectangular solid is cut open and flattened out, each face is a rectangle. The surface area, *SA*, of the rectangular solid is the sum of the areas of the six rectangles:

$$SA = LW + LH + WH + \\ LW + WH + LH$$

which simplifies to

$$SA = 2LW + 2LH + 2WH$$

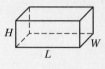

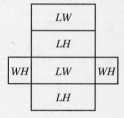

The surface area of a cube is the sum of the areas of the six faces of the cube. The area of each face is s^2. Therefore, the surface area, *SA*, of a cube is given by the formula $SA = 6s^2$.

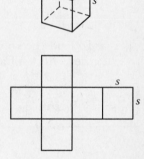

When a cylinder is cut open and flattened out, the top and bottom of the cylinder are circles. The side of the cylinder flattens out to a rectangle. The length of the rectangle is the circumference of the base, which is $2\pi r$; the width is h, the height of the cylinder. Therefore, the area of the rectangle is $2\pi rh$. The surface area, *SA*, of the cylinder is

$$SA = \pi r^2 + 2\pi rh + \pi r^2$$

which simplifies to

$$SA = 2\pi r^2 + 2\pi rh$$

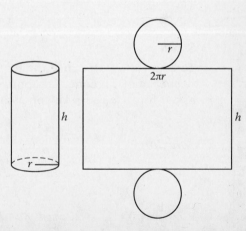

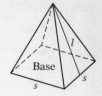

The surface area of a pyramid is the area of the base plus the area of the four isosceles triangles. A side of the square base is s; therefore, the area of the base is s^2. The slant height, l, is the height of each triangle, and s is the base of each triangle. The surface area, SA, of a pyramid is

$$SA = s^2 + 4\left(\frac{1}{2}sl\right)$$

which simplifies to

$$SA = s^2 + 2sl$$

Formulas for the surface areas of geometric solids are given below.

Surface Areas of Geometric Solids

The surface area, SA, of a **rectangular solid** with length L, width W, and height H is given by $SA = 2LW + 2LH + 2WH$.

The surface area, SA, of a **cube** with side s is given by $SA = 6s^2$.

The surface area, SA, of a **sphere** with radius r is given by $SA = 4\pi r^2$.

The surface area, SA, of a **right circular cylinder** is given by $SA = 2\pi r^2 + 2\pi rh$, where r is the radius of the base and h is the height.

The surface area, SA, of a **right circular cone** is given by $SA = \pi r^2 + \pi rl$, where r is the radius of the circular base and l is the slant height.

The surface area, SA, of a **regular pyramid** is given by $SA = s^2 + 2sl$, where s is the length of a side of the base and l is the slant height.

Find the surface area of a sphere with a diameter of 18 cm.

First find the radius of the sphere.

$$r = \frac{1}{2}d = \frac{1}{2}(18) = 9$$

Use the formula for the surface area of a sphere.

$$SA = 4\pi r^2$$
$$SA = 4\pi(9)^2$$
$$SA = 4\pi(81)$$
$$SA = 324\pi$$

The exact surface area of the sphere is 324π cm². An approximate measure can be found by using the π key on a calculator.

$$SA \approx 1{,}017.88$$

The approximate surface area is 1,017.88 cm².

Example 5

The diameter of the base of a cone is 5 m and the slant height is 4 m. Find the surface area of the cone. Give the exact measure.

Strategy

To find the surface area of the cone:
▶ Find the radius of the base of the cone.
▶ Use the formula for the surface area of a cone. Leave the answer in terms of π.

Solution

$r = \dfrac{1}{2}d = \dfrac{1}{2}(5) = 2.5$

$SA = \pi r^2 + \pi r l$
$SA = \pi(2.5)^2 + \pi(2.5)(4)$
$SA = \pi(6.25) + \pi(2.5)(4)$
$SA = 6.25\pi + 10\pi$
$SA = 16.25\pi$

The surface area of the cone is 16.25π m^2.

Example 6

The diameter of the base of a cylinder is 6 ft and the height is 8 ft. Find the surface area of the cylinder. Round to the nearest hundredth.

Your Strategy

Your Solution

Example 7

Find the area of a label used to cover a soup can that has a radius of 4 cm and a height of 12 cm. The size of the label must allow for 1 cm of overlap so that the label can be glued on. Round to the nearest hundredth.

Strategy

To find the area of the label, use the fact that the surface area of the sides of a cylinder is given by $2\pi rh$. Since the label must overlap 1 cm, add 1 cm to the circumference of the base. The circumference of the base is $2\pi r$. An approximation is asked for; use the π key on a calculator. $r = 4$, $h = 12$.

Solution

Area of the label $= (2\pi r + 1)h$
$\qquad\qquad\quad = (2\pi \cdot 4 + 1)(12)$
$\qquad\qquad\quad = (8\pi + 1)(12)$
$\qquad\qquad\quad = 96\pi + 12 \approx 313.59$

The area of the label is 313.59 cm^2.

Example 8

Which has a larger surface area, a cube with a side measuring 10 cm or a sphere with a diameter measuring 8 cm?

Your Strategy

Your Solution

Solutions on p. A7

5 EXERCISES

▶ **Objective A**

Find the volume of each figure.
For calculations involving π, give both the exact value and an approximation to the nearest hundredth.

1.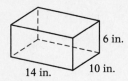
6 in.
14 in.   10 in.

2.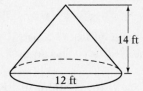
14 ft
12 ft

3.
5 ft
3 ft
3 ft

4.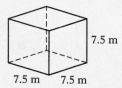
7.5 m
7.5 m   7.5 m

5.
3 cm

6.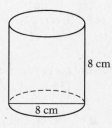
8 cm
8 cm

Solve.

7. A rectangular solid has a length of 6.8 m, a width of 2.5 m, and a height of 2 m. Find the volume of the solid.

8. Find the volume of a rectangular solid that has a length of 4.5 ft, a width of 3 ft, and a height of 1.5 ft.

9. Find the volume of a cube whose side measures 2.5 in.

10. The length of a side of a cube is 7 cm. Find the volume of the cube.

11. The diameter of a sphere is 6 ft. Find the volume of the sphere. Give the exact measure.

12. Find the volume of a sphere that has a radius of 2.25 m. Round to the nearest hundredth.

13. The diameter of the base of a cylinder is 24 cm. The height of the cylinder is 18 cm. Find the volume of the cylinder. Round to the nearest hundredth.

14. The height of a cylinder is 7.2 m. The radius of the base is 4 m. Find the volume of the cylinder. Give the exact measure.

15. The radius of the base of a cone is 5 in. The height of the cone is 9 in. Find the volume of the cone. Give the exact measure.

16. The height of a cone is 15 cm. The diameter of the cone is 10 cm. Find the volume of the cone. Round to the nearest hundredth.

Solve.

17. The length of a side of the base of a pyramid is 6 in. and the height is 10 in. Find the volume of the pyramid.

18. The height of a pyramid is 8 m and the length of a side of the base is 9 m. What is the volume of the pyramid?

19. The volume of a freezer with a length of 7 ft and a height of 3 ft is 52.5 ft³. Find the width of the freezer.

20. The length of an aquarium is 18 in. and the width is 12 in. If the volume of the aquarium is 1,836 in³, what is the height of the aquarium?

21. The volume of a cylinder with a height of 10 in. is 502.4 in³. Find the radius of the base of the cylinder. Round to the nearest hundredth.

22. The diameter of the base of a cylinder is 14 cm. If the volume of the cylinder is 2,310 cm³, find the height of the cylinder. Round to the nearest hundredth.

23. A rectangular solid has a square base and a height of 5 in. If the volume of the solid is 125 in³, find the length and the width.

24. The volume of a rectangular solid is 864 m³. The rectangular solid has a square base and a height of 6 m. Find the dimensions of the solid.

25. An oil storage tank, which is in the shape of a cylinder, is 4 m high and has a diameter of 6 m. The oil tank is two-thirds full. Find the number of cubic meters of oil in the tank. Round to the nearest hundredth.

26. A silo, which is in the shape of a cylinder, is 16 ft in diameter and has a height of 30 ft. The silo is three-fourths full. Find the volume of the portion of the silo that is not being used for storage. Round to the nearest hundredth.

27. What is the effect on the volume of a rectangular solid if both the length and the width are doubled?

28. What is the effect on the volume of a cube if the length of each side of the cube is doubled?

▶ **Objective B**

Find the surface area of each figure.

29.   30.   31.

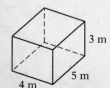

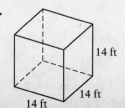

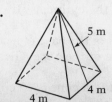

Find the surface area of each figure.
Give both the exact value and an approximation to the nearest hundredth.

32. 2 cm

33. 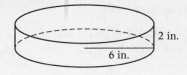 2 in. / 6 in.

34.  9 ft / 3 ft

Solve.

35. The height of a rectangular solid is 5 ft. The length is 8 ft, and the width is 4 ft. Find the surface area of the solid.

36. The width of a rectangular solid is 32 cm. The length is 60 cm, and the height is 14 cm. What is the surface area of the solid?

37. The side of a cube measures 3.4 m. Find the surface area of the cube.

38. Find the surface area of a cube that has a side measuring 1.5 in.

39. Find the surface area of a sphere with a diameter of 15 cm. Give the exact value.

40. The radius of a sphere is 2 in. Find the surface area of the sphere. Round to the nearest hundredth.

41. The radius of the base of a cylinder is 4 in. The height of the cylinder is 12 in. Find the surface area of the cylinder. Round to the nearest hundredth.

42. The diameter of the base of a cylinder is 1.8 m. The height of the cylinder is 0.7 m. Find the surface area of the cylinder. Give the exact value.

43. The slant height of a cone is 2.5 ft. The radius of the base is 1.5 ft. Find the surface area of the cone. Give the exact value.

44. The diameter of the base of a cone is 21 in. The slant height is 16 in. What is the surface area of the cone? Round to the nearest hundredth.

45. The length of a side of the base of a pyramid is 9 in., and the slant height is 12 in. Find the surface area of the pyramid.

46. The slant height of a pyramid is 18 m, and the length of a side of the base is 16 m. What is the surface area of the pyramid?

47. The surface area of a rectangular solid is 108 cm². The height of the solid is 4 cm, and the length is 6 cm. Find the width of the rectangular solid.

Solve.

48. The length of a rectangular solid is 12 ft. The width is 3 ft. If the surface area is 162 ft², find the height of the rectangular solid.

49. A can of paint will cover 300 ft². How many cans of paint should be purchased in order to paint a cylinder that has a height of 30 ft and a radius of 12 ft?

50. A can of paint will cover 100 m². How many cans of paint should be purchased in order to paint a sphere with a radius of 30 m?

51. A hot-air balloon is in the shape of a sphere. Approximately how much fabric was used to construct the balloon if its diameter is 32 ft? Round to the nearest whole number.

52. How much glass is needed to make a fish tank that is 12 in. long, 8 in. wide, and 9 in. high? The fish tank is open at the top.

53. Find the area of a label used to cover a can of juice that has a diameter of 16.5 cm and a height of 17 cm. The size of the label must allow for 1 cm overlap so that the label can be glued on. Round to the nearest hundredth.

54. The length of a side of the base of a pyramid is 5 cm and the slant height is 8 cm. How much larger is the surface area of this pyramid than the surface area of a cone with a diameter of 5 cm and a slant height of 8 cm? Round to the nearest hundredth.

55. What is the effect on the surface area of a cylinder if the radius and height are doubled?

▶ *Supplemental Exercises*

56. Half of a sphere is called a **hemisphere**. Derive formulas for the volume and surface area of a hemisphere.

57. Determine whether each statement is always true, sometimes true, or never true.
   a. The slant height of a regular pyramid is longer than the height.
   b. The slant height of a cone is shorter than the height.
   c. The height of a rectangular solid is greater than the length.
   d. The four triangular faces of a regular pyramid are equilateral triangles.

[w] **58.** Explain how you could cut through a cube so that the face of the resulting solid is **a.** a square, **b.** an equilateral triangle, **c.** a trapezoid, **d.** a hexagon.

59. What is the effect on the surface area of a rectangular solid if the width and height are doubled?

60. A box has a length of 4 in., a width of 3 in., and height of 2 in. Find the distance from one corner of the box to the diagonally opposite corner (the distance from *A* to *D* in the diagram at the right).

[w] **61.** Prepare a report on the rods and cones at the back of the retina. Describe the difference in the way each perceives color.

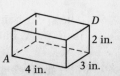

SECTION **6**   **Composite Figures**

OBJECTIVE **A**   **Perimeter of a composite plane figure**

Composite geometric figures are made from two or more geometric figures. The following composite figure is made from part of a rectangle and part of a circle.

Composite figure = 3 sides of a rectangle + $\dfrac{1}{2}$ the circumference of a circle

Perimeter   = $2L + W$ $+ \dfrac{1}{2}\pi d$

Find the perimeter of the composite figure shown above if the width of the rectangle is 4 m and the length of the rectangle is 8 m. Round to the nearest hundredth.

Use the equation given above. $L = 8$, $W = 4$. The diameter of the circle equals the width of the rectangle, 4. Use the π key on a calculator to approximate the perimeter.

$P = 2L + W + \dfrac{1}{2}\pi d$
$P = 2(8) + 4 + \dfrac{1}{2}\pi(4)$
$P = 20 + 2\pi$
$P \approx 26.28$

To the nearest hundredth, the perimeter of the figure is 26.28 m.

Example 1

Find the perimeter of the figure. Round to the nearest hundredth.

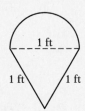

1 ft

1 ft   1 ft

Example 2

The circumference of the circle in the figure is 6π cm. Find the perimeter of square *ABCD*.

Strategy

The perimeter is equal to 2 sides of a triangle plus $\dfrac{1}{2}$ the circumference of a circle. An approximation is asked for; use the π key on a calculator.

Your Strategy

Solution

$P = a + b + \dfrac{1}{2}\pi d$

$P = 1 + 1 + \dfrac{1}{2}\pi(1) = 2 + 0.5\pi \approx 3.57$

The perimeter is 3.57 ft.

Your Solution

Solution on p. A7

OBJECTIVE B | Area of a composite plane figure

The area of the composite figure shown below is found by calculating the area of the rectangle and then subtracting the area of the triangle.

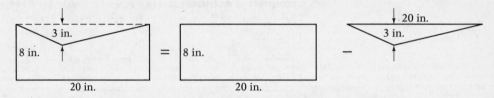

▮ Area of the composite figure = area of the rectangle − area of the triangle

$$= \quad LW \quad - \quad \frac{1}{2}bh$$

$$= \quad 20(8) \quad - \quad \frac{1}{2}(20)(3)$$

$$= \quad 160 \quad - \quad 30$$

$$= \quad 130$$

The area of the composite figure is 130 in².

Example 3

Find the area of the shaded portion of the figure. Round to the nearest hundredth.

Example 4

Find the area of the composite figure.

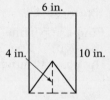

Strategy

The area is equal to the area of the square minus the area of the circle. The radius of the circle is one-half the length of a side of the square (8). An approximation is asked for; use the π key on a calculator.

Your Strategy

Solution

$$r = \frac{1}{2}s = \frac{1}{2}(8) = 4$$

$$A = s^2 - \pi r^2$$
$$A = (8)^2 - \pi(4)^2 = 64 - 16\pi \approx 13.73$$

The area of the shaded portion of the figure is 13.73 m².

Your Solution

Solution on p. A7

OBJECTIVE **C**   Volume of a composite solid

Composite geometric solids are solids made from two or more geometric solids. The following solid is made from a cylinder and one half of a sphere.

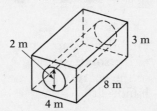

Composite solid   =   a cylinder   +   one-half of a sphere

Volume of the composite solid   = $\pi r^2 h$ + $\dfrac{1}{2} \cdot \dfrac{4}{3} \pi r^3$

■ Find the volume of the solid shown above if the radius of the base of the cylinder is 3 in. and the height of the cylinder is 10 in. Give the exact measure.

Use the equation given above. $r = 3$, $h = 10$. The radius of the sphere equals the radius of the base of the cylinder, 3.

$$V = \pi r^2 h + \frac{1}{2} \cdot \frac{4}{3} \pi r^3$$

$$V = \pi (3)^2 (10) + \frac{1}{2} \cdot \frac{4}{3} \pi (3)^3$$

$$V = \pi (9)(10) + \frac{2}{3} \pi (27)$$

$$V = 90\pi + 18\pi$$
$$V = 108\pi$$

The volume of the solid is 108π in³.

Example 5

Find the volume of the solid. Round to the nearest hundredth.

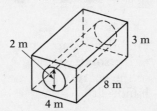

Example 6

Find the volume of the solid. Give the exact measure.

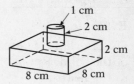

Strategy

The volume is equal to the volume of the rectangular solid minus the volume of the cylinder. The radius of the circle is one-half the diameter of the circle. An approximation is asked for; use the π key on a calculator.

Your Strategy

Solution

$$r = \frac{1}{2}d = \frac{1}{2}(2) = 1$$

$$V = LWH - \pi r^2 h$$
$$V = 4(8)(3) - \pi(1)^2(8) = 96 - 8\pi \approx 70.87$$

The volume of the solid is 70.87 m³.

Your Solution

Solution on p. A8

68   *A Review of Geometry*

OBJECTIVE D   **Surface area of a composite solid**

The composite solid shown below is made from a cone, a cylinder, and one-half of a sphere.

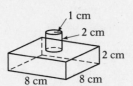

Composite solid = a cone + a cylinder + one-half of a sphere

Surface area of the solid = the surface area of a cone minus the base + the surface area of the sides of a cylinder + one-half of the surface area of a sphere

$$= \pi r l \quad + \quad 2\pi r h \quad + \quad \frac{1}{2}(4\pi r^2)$$

Find the surface area of the solid shown above if the radius of the base of the cylinder is 4 in. and the height is 5 in. The slant height of the cone is 3 in. Give the exact measure.

Use the equation given above. $r = 4, h = 5, l = 3$. The radius of the base of the cone and the radius of the sphere equal the radius of the base of the cylinder, 4.

$SA = \pi r l + 2\pi r h + \frac{1}{2}(4\pi r^2)$

$SA = \pi(4)(3) + 2\pi(4)(5) + \frac{1}{2}[4\pi(4)^2]$

$SA = \pi(12) + 40\pi + 2\pi(16)$

$SA = 12\pi + 40\pi + 32\pi = 84\pi$

The surface area of the solid is 84π in².

Example 7

Find the surface area of the solid. Round to the nearest hundredth.

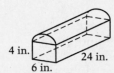

Strategy

The total surface area equals the surface area of the rectangular solid, minus the bottom of the cylinder, plus the surface area of the cylinder, minus the bottom of the cylinder.

Solution

$SA = 2LW + 2LH + 2HW - \pi r^2 + 2\pi r^2 + 2\pi r h - \pi r^2$

$SA = 2LW + 2LH + 2HW + 2\pi r h$

$SA = 2(8)(8) + 2(8)(2) + 2(2)(8) + 2\pi(1)(2)$

$SA = 128 + 32 + 32 + 4\pi$

$SA = 192 + 4\pi \approx 204.57$

The surface area of the solid is 204.57 cm².

Example 8

Find the surface area of the solid. Round to the nearest hundredth.

Your Strategy

Your Solution

Solution on p. A8

6 EXERCISES

▶ **Objective A**

Find the perimeter of each composite figure. For calculations involving π, give both the exact value and an approximation to the nearest hundredth.

1.
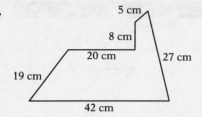

2.
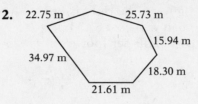

3.
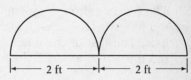

4.
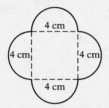

5.
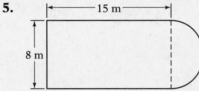

6.
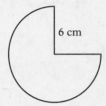

7.
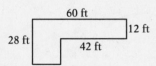

8.
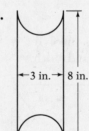

9.
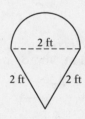

10.
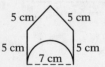

11.
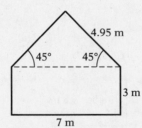

12.

Solve.

13. Find the length of weather stripping installed around the arched door shown in the figure at the right. Round to the nearest hundredth.

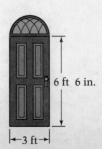

Solve.

14. Find the perimeter of the roller rink shown in the figure at the right. Round to the nearest hundredth.

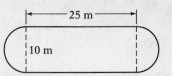

15. The rectangular lot shown in the figure at the right is being fenced. The fencing along the road will cost $2.70 per foot. The rest of the fencing will cost $2.10 per foot. Find the total cost to fence the lot.

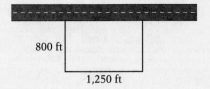

16. A rain gutter is being installed on a home that has the dimensions shown in the figure at the right. At a cost of $11.30 per meter, how much will it cost to install the rain gutter?

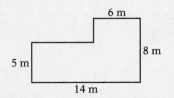

▶ **Objective B**

Find the area of each composite figure. For calculations involving π, give both the exact value and an approximation to the nearest hundredth.

17.

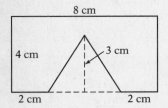

18.

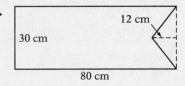

19.

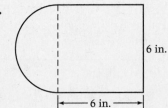

20.

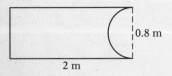

21.

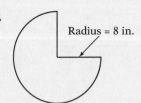

22.

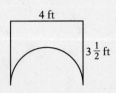

23.

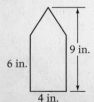

24.

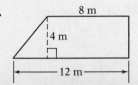

25.

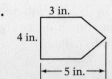

Find the area of each composite figure. For calculations involving π, give both the exact value and an approximation to the nearest hundredth.

26.
22 cm
22 cm

27.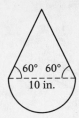
60° 60°
10 in.

28.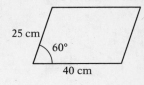
25 cm
60°
40 cm

Solve.

29. A carpet is to be installed in one room and a hallway, as shown in the diagram at the right. At a cost of $18.50 per square meter, how much will it cost to carpet the area?

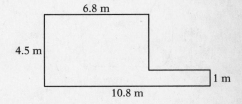
6.8 m
4.5 m
1 m
10.8 m

30. Find the area of the 2-meter boundary around the swimming pool shown in the figure at the right.

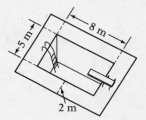
5 m
8 m
2 m

31. How much hardwood floor is needed to cover the roller rink shown in the figure at the right? Round to the nearest hundredth.

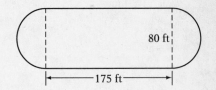
80 ft
175 ft

32. Find the total area of a national park with the dimensions shown in the figure at the right. Round to the nearest hundredth.

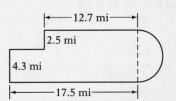
12.7 mi
2.5 mi
4.3 mi
17.5 mi

▶ **Objective C**

Find the volume of each composite figure.
For calculations involving π, give both the exact value and an approximation to the nearest hundredth.

33.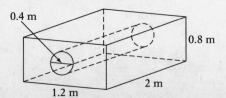
0.4 m
0.8 m
1.2 m
2 m

34.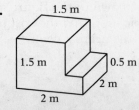
1.5 m
1.5 m
0.5 m
2 m
2 m

35.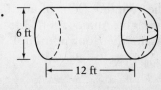
6 ft
12 ft

Find the volume of each composite figure.
For calculations involving π, give both the exact value and an approximation
to the nearest hundredth.

36.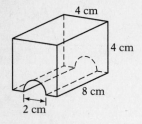

37.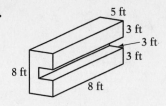

38.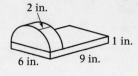

39.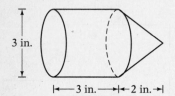

40.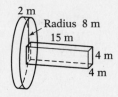

41.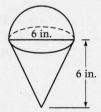

42.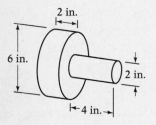

43.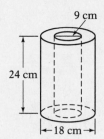

44.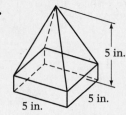

Solve.

45. Find the volume of the bushing shown in the figure at the
right. Round to the nearest hundredth.

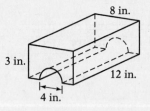

46. An eighteen-wheeler is carrying an oil tank, as shown in
the figure at the right. If the tank is half full, how many
cubic feet of oil is the truck carrying? Round to the
nearest hundredth.

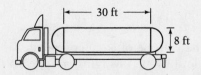

47. The concrete floor of a building is shown in the figure at
the right. At a cost of $3.15 per cubic foot, find the cost of
having the floor poured. Round to the nearest cent.

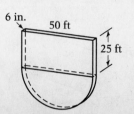

Solve.

48. How many liters of water are needed to fill the swimming pool shown at the right? (1 m³ contains 1,000 L.)

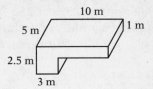

▶ **Objective D**

Find the surface area of each composite figure. For calculations involving π, give both the exact value and an approximation to the nearest hundredth.

49.

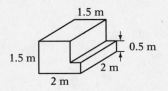

50.

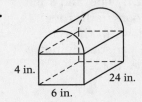

51.

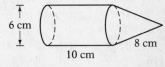

52.

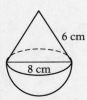

53.

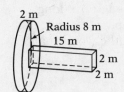

54.

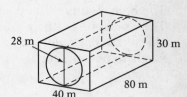

55.

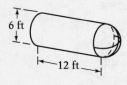

56.

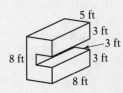

57.

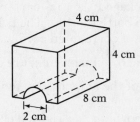

58.

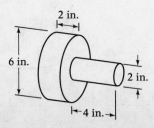

59.

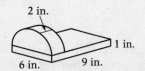

60.

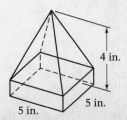

Solve.

61. A can of paint will cover 250 ft². Find the number of cans of paint that should be purchased in order to paint the exterior of the auditorium shown in the figure at the right.

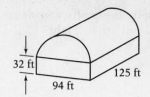
32 ft
94 ft
125 ft

62. A piece of sheet metal is cut and formed into the shape shown at the right. Given that there are 0.24 g in 1 cm² of the metal, find the total number of grams of metal used. Round to the nearest hundredth.

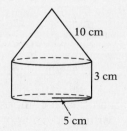
10 cm
3 cm
5 cm

63. The walls of a room that is 25.5 ft long, 22 ft wide, and 8 ft high are being plastered. There are two doors in the room, each 2.5 ft by 7 ft. Each of the six windows in the room measures 2.5 ft by 4 ft. At a cost of $.75 per square foot, find the cost of plastering the walls of the room.

64. You plan on painting the bookcase shown at the right. The bookcase is 10 in. deep, 36 in. high, and 36 in. long. The wood is 1 in. thick. You do not plan to paint the back side or the bottom. Find the surface area of the wood that needs to be painted.

▶ *Supplemental Exercises*

65. Bottles of apple juice are being packaged six to a carton for shipping. The diameter of the base of the bottles is 4 in. The height of the bottles is 8 in. The cartons are made of corrugated cardboard that is $\frac{1}{8}$ inch thick. Pieces of cardboard, each $\frac{1}{16}$ inch thick, are placed between bottles. Find the dimensions of the shipping carton.

66. A sphere fits inside a cylinder as shown at the right. The height of the cylinder equals the diameter of the ball. Show that the surface area of the sphere equals the surface area of the sides of the cylinder.

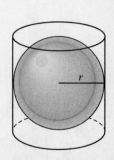
r

[w] **67.** Explain the meaning of the "vanishing point" in a drawing. Find examples of its use.

[w] **68.** Prepare a report on the use of geometric form in architecture. Include examples of both plane geometric figures and geometric solids.

[w] **69.** Write a paper on the artist M.C. Escher. Explain how he used mathematics and geometry in his works.

Summary of Terms and Formulas

Key Words   A *line* is determined by two distinct points and extends indefinitely in both directions. A *line segment* is part of a line that has two endpoints. *Parallel lines* never meet; the distance between them is always the same. *Perpendicular lines* are intersecting lines that form right angles.

A *ray* is a half-line that includes its endpoint. An *angle* is formed by two rays with the same endpoint. The *vertex* of an angle is the point at which the two rays meet. An angle is measured in *degrees*. A 90° angle is a *right angle*. A 180° angle is a *straight angle*.

Complementary angles are two angles whose measures have the sum 90°. *Supplementary angles* are two angles whose measures have the sum 180°. An *acute angle* is an angle whose measure is between 0° and 90°. An *obtuse angle* is an angle whose measure is between 90° and 180°.

Two angles that are on opposite sides of the intersection of two lines are *vertical angles*. Two angles that share a common side are *adjacent angles*.

A line that intersects two other lines at two different points is a *transversal*. If the lines cut by a transversal are parallel lines, equal angles are formed: *alternate interior angles, alternate exterior angles*, and *corresponding angles*.

A *polygon* is a closed figure determined by three or more line segments. The line segments that form the polygon are its *sides*. A *regular polygon* is one in which each side has the same length. A *vertex* of a polygon is a point at which two line segments meet. An angle at the vertex of a polygon is an *interior angle*. An *exterior angle* is an angle that is adjacent to an interior angle. The endpoints of one side of a polygon are *adjacent vertices*. A *diagonal* of a polygon is a line segment joining two nonadjacent vertices. Polygons are classified by the number of sides.

A *triangle* is a plane figure formed by three line segments. An *isosceles triangle* has two sides of equal length. The three sides of an *equilateral triangle* are of equal length. A *scalene triangle* has no two sides of equal length. An *acute triangle* has three acute angles. An *obtuse triangle* has one obtuse angle. A *right triangle* has a right angle; the side opposite the right angle is the *hypotenuse;* the other two sides are *legs*. *Similar triangles* have the same shape but not necessarily the same size. *Congruent triangles* have the same shape and the same size.

A *quadrilateral* is a four-sided polygon. A parallelogram, a rectangle, a square, a rhombus, and a trapezoid are all quadrilaterals.

A *circle* is a plane figure in which all points are the same distance from the center of the circle. A *diameter* of a circle is a line segment across the circle through the center. A *radius* of a circle is a line segment from the center of the circle to a point on the circle. The distance around a circle is the *circumference*.

The *perimeter* of a plane geometric figure is a measure of the distance around the figure. *Area* is the amount of surface in a region. *Volume* is a measure of the amount of space inside a figure in space. The *surface area* of a solid is the total area on the surface of the solid.

Composite geometric figures are figures made from two or more geometric figures.

Essential Rules

Triangles

45°–45°–90°: $c = \sqrt{2}$ (length of a leg)

30°–60°–90°: $c = 2$ (length of shorter leg)

length of longer leg $= \sqrt{3}$ (length of shorter leg)

Rules to determine congruence: SSS Rule
SAS Rule
ASA Rule

Perimeter

Triangle: $P = a + b + c$
Rectangle: $P = 2L + 2W$
Square: $P = 4s$
Circle: $C = \pi d$ or $C = 2\pi r$

Area

Triangle: $A = \dfrac{1}{2}bh$

Rectangle: $A = LW$

Square: $A = s^2$

Circle: $A = \pi r^2$

Parallelogram: $A = bh$

Trapezoid: $A = \dfrac{1}{2}h(b_1 + b_2)$

Volume

Rectangular solid: $V = LWH$
Cube: $V = s^3$

Sphere: $V = \dfrac{4}{3}\pi r^3$

Right circular cylinder: $V = \pi r^2 h$

Right circular cone: $V = \dfrac{1}{3}\pi r^2 h$

Regular pyramid: $V = \dfrac{1}{3}s^2 h$

Surface Area

Rectangular solid: $SA = 2LW + 2LH + 2WH$
Cube: $SA = 6s^2$
Sphere: $SA = 4\pi r^2$
Right circular cylinder: $SA = 2\pi r^2 + 2\pi rh$
Right circular cone: $SA = \pi r^2 + \pi rl$
Regular pyramid: $SA = s^2 + 2sl$

Sum of the Measures of the Interior Angles of a Polygon with n sides:
$(n - 2)180°$

Square Root Property

If $r^2 = s$, then $r = \sqrt{s}$ or $r = -\sqrt{s}$, and r is called the square root of s.

Pythagorean Theorem

If a and b are the legs of a right triangle and c is the length of the hypotenuse, then $c^2 = a^2 + b^2$.

Similar Triangles

Corresponding angles are equal.
The ratios of corresponding sides are equal.
The ratio of corresponding heights is equal to the ratio of corresponding sides.

Review Exercises

1. Given that $\angle a = 74°$ and $\angle b = 52°$, find the measure of angles x and y.

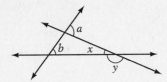

2. Determine whether or not the two triangles are congruent. If they are congruent, state by what rule they are congruent.

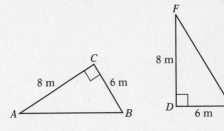

3. Find the volume of the composite figure.

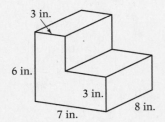

4. Find the measure of $\angle x$.

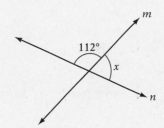

5. Find the hypotenuse of the right triangle.

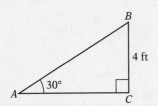

6. Find the surface area of the composite figure. Round to the nearest hundredth.

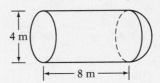

7. Find the circumference of the circle. Give the exact value.

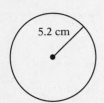

8. Find the unknown side of the triangle. Round to the nearest hundredth.

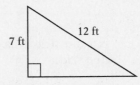

9. Find the area of the composite figure. Round to the nearest hundredth.

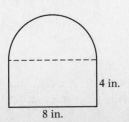

10. Find the volume of the figure.

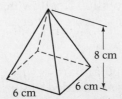

11. Find the perimeter of the composite figure. Round to the nearest hundredth.

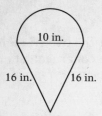

12. Given that $l_1 \parallel l_2$, find the measures of angles a and b.

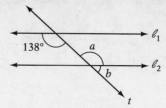

13. Triangles *ABC* and *DEF* are similar. Find the perimeter of triangle *ABC*.

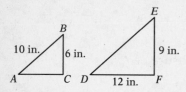

14. Find x.

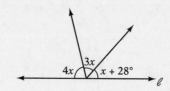

15. Find the surface area of the figure.

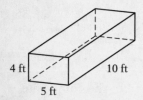

16. Find the area of the circle. Round to the nearest hundredth.

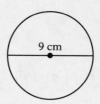

Solve.

17. Find the supplement of a 32° angle.

18. Find the measure of each interior angle of a regular nonagon.

19. Two angles of a triangle measure 37° and 48°. Find the measure of the third angle.

20. The height of a triangle is 7 cm. The area of the triangle is 28 cm². Find the length of the base of the triangle.

21. The length of a side of a square is 10 in. Find the length of a diagonal of the square. Round to the nearest hundredth.

22. A can of paint will cover 200 ft². How many cans of paint should be purchased in order to paint a cylinder that has a height of 15 ft and a radius of 6 ft?

23. The length of a rectangular park is 56 yd. The width is 48 yd. How many yards of fencing are needed to surround the park?

24. What is the area of a square patio that measures 9.5 m on each side?

Appendix

Solutions to Examples

Section 1 *(pages 3 - 12)*

Example 2
$$QR + RS + ST = QT$$
$$24 + RS + 17 = 62$$
$$41 + RS = 62$$
$$RS = 21$$

$$RS = 21 \text{ cm}$$

Example 4
$$AC = AB + BC$$
$$AC = \frac{1}{4}(BC) + BC$$
$$AC = \frac{1}{4}(16) + 16 = 4 + 16 = 20$$
$$AC = 20 \text{ ft}$$

Example 6
Strategy
Supplementary angles are two angles whose sum is 180°. To find the supplement, let x represent the supplement of a 129° angle. Write an equation and solve for x.

Solution
$$x + 129° = 180°$$
$$x = 51°$$

The supplement of a 129° angle is a 51° angle.

Example 8
Strategy
To find the measure of $\angle a$, write an equation using the fact that the sum of the measures of $\angle a$ and 68° is 118°. Solve for $\angle a$.

Solution
$$\angle a + 68° = 118°$$
$$\angle a = 50°$$

The measure of $\angle a$ is 50°.

Example 10
Strategy
The angles labeled are adjacent angles of intersecting lines and are, therefore, supplementary angles. To find x, write an equation and solve for x.

Solution
$$(x + 15°) + 2x = 180°$$
$$3x + 15° = 180°$$
$$3x = 165°$$
$$x = 55°$$

Example 12
Strategy
$3x = y$ because corresponding angles have the same measure. $y + (x + 40°) = 180°$ because adjacent angles of intersecting lines are supplementary angles. Substitute $3x$ for y and solve for x.

Solution
$$3x + (x + 40°) = 180°$$
$$4x + 40° = 180°$$
$$4x = 140°$$
$$x = 35°$$

Example 14
Strategy
▶ To find the measure of angle b, use the fact that $\angle b$ and $\angle x$ are supplementary angles.
▶ To find the measure of angle c, use the fact that the sum of the interior angles of a triangle is 180°.
▶ To find the measure of angle y, use the fact that $\angle c$ and $\angle y$ are vertical angles.

Solution
$$\angle b + \angle x = 180°$$
$$\angle b + 100° = 180°$$
$$\angle b = 80°$$

$$\angle a + \angle b + \angle c = 180°$$
$$45° + 80° + \angle c = 180°$$
$$125° + \angle c = 180°$$
$$\angle c = 55°$$

$$\angle y = \angle c = 55°$$

Example 16
Strategy
To find the measure of the third angle, use the facts that the measure of a right angle is 90° and the sum of the measures of the interior angles of a triangle is 180°. Write an equation using x to represent the measure of the third angle. Solve the equation for x.

Solution
$$x + 90° + 34° = 180°$$
$$x + 124° = 180°$$
$$x = 56°$$

The measure of the third angle is 56°.

Section 2 *(pages 19 - 28)*

Example 2
Figure A is not composed of line segments and, therefore, is not a polygon. In Figure C, line segments do not meet at their endpoints; therefore, Figure C is not a polygon. Figure B is a polygon.

Example 4
Strategy
Let x represent the measure of the exterior angle. Write an equation using the fact that the sum of the measures of an interior angle and a corresponding exterior angle is 180°.

Solution
$$x + 98° = 180°$$
$$x = 82°$$

The measure of the exterior angle is 82°.

Example 6
Strategy
To find the measure of each interior angle:
▶ Use the formula for the sum of the measures of the interior angles of a polygon to find the sum of the measures of the interior angles of a dodecagon. A dodecagon has 12 sides; $n = 12$.
▶ Divide the sum of the measures of the interior angles of a dodecagon by the number of angles, 12.

Solution
$(n - 2)180° = (12 - 2)180° = (10)180° = 1,800°$

$1,800° \div 12 = 150°$

Each interior angle of a regular dodecagon measures 150°.

Example 8
Strategy
To find the perimeter, use the formula for the perimeter of a square. Substitute 60 for s and solve for P.

Solution
$P = 4s = 4(60) = 240$

The perimeter of the infield is 240 ft.

Example 10
Strategy
To find the perimeter, use the formula for the perimeter of a rectangle. Substitute 11 for L and $8\frac{1}{2}$ for W and solve for L.

Solution
$P = 2L + 2W$

$P = 2(11) + 2\left(8\frac{1}{2}\right) = 2(11) + 2\left(\frac{17}{2}\right) = 22 + 17 = 39$

The perimeter of a standard piece of typing paper is 39 in.

Example 12
Strategy
To find the number of rolls of wallpaper to be purchased:
▶ Use the formula for the area of a rectangle to find the area of one wall.
▶ Multiply the area of one wall by the number of walls to be covered (2).
▶ Divide the area of wall to be covered by the area one roll of wallpaper will cover (30).

Solution

$A = LW = 12 \cdot 8 = 96$	The area of one wall is 96 ft².
$2(96) = 192$	The area of the two walls is 192 ft².

$192 \div 30 = 6.4$

Because a portion of a seventh roll is needed, 7 rolls of wallpaper should be purchased.

Section 3 *(pages 35 - 44)*

Example 2

Strategy

To find the measure of the other leg, use the Pythagorean Theorem. $a = 2.6$, $c = 3.2$

Solution

$$a^2 + b^2 = c^2$$
$$(2.6)^2 + b^2 = (3.2)^2$$
$$6.76 + b^2 = 10.24$$
$$b^2 = 3.48$$
$$b = \sqrt{3.48}$$
$$b \approx 1.87$$

The measure of the other leg is approximately 1.87 m.

Example 4

Strategy

▶ To find the measure of the longer leg, multiply the length of the shorter leg (4) by $\sqrt{3}$.
▶ To find the length of the hypotenuse, multiply the length of the shorter leg (4) by 2.

Solution

length of the longer leg = (length of the shorter leg)$\sqrt{3}$
$$= 4\sqrt{3}$$

$c = 2$(length of the shorter leg) $= 2(4) = 8$

The other two sides of the triangle measure $4\sqrt{3}$ in. and 8 in.

Example 6

Strategy

To find the perimeter of the triangle:
▶ Use the relationships between the sides of an isosceles right triangle to find the length of the hypotenuse.
▶ Use the formula for the perimeter of a triangle.

Solution

$$c = \sqrt{2}(\text{length of a leg}) = \sqrt{2}(4) = 4\sqrt{2}$$

$$P = a + b + c$$
$$P = 4 + 4 + 4\sqrt{2} \approx 4 + 4 + 5.7 \approx 13.7$$

The perimeter of the triangle is approximately 13.7 cm.

Example 8

Strategy

To find the area:
▶ Use the relationships between the sides of a 30°–60°–90° triangle to find the length of the legs of the triangle.
▶ Use the formula for the area of a triangle. Let side AC be the base and side BC be the height.

Solution

$$c = 2(\text{length of the shorter leg})$$
$$16 = 2(AC)$$
$$8 = AC$$

$$BC = (\text{length of the shorter leg})\sqrt{3} = (AC)\sqrt{3} = 8\sqrt{3}$$

$$A = \frac{1}{2}bh = \frac{1}{2}(8)(8\sqrt{3}) = 4(8\sqrt{3}) \approx 55.4$$

The area of the triangle is approximately 55.4 ft^2.

Example 10

Strategy

To find FG, write a proportion using the fact that, in similar triangles, the ratio of corresponding sides equals the ratio of corresponding heights. Solve the proportion for FG.

Solution

$$\frac{AC}{DF} = \frac{CH}{FG}$$
$$\frac{10}{15} = \frac{7}{FG}$$
$$10(FG) = 15(7)$$
$$10(FG) = 105$$
$$F = 10.5$$

The height FG of triangle DEF is 10.5 m.

Example 12

Strategy

To find the perimeter of triangle ABC:
▶ Solve two proportions, one to find side BC and one to find side AC.
▶ Use the formula for the perimeter of a triangle.

Solution

$$\frac{AB}{DE} = \frac{BC}{EF} \qquad \frac{AB}{DE} = \frac{AC}{DF}$$
$$\frac{4}{8} = \frac{BC}{10} \qquad \frac{4}{8} = \frac{AC}{6}$$
$$4(10) = 8(BC) \qquad 4(6) = 8(AC)$$
$$40 = 8(BC) \qquad 24 = 8(AC)$$
$$5 = BC \qquad 3 = AC$$

$$P = a + b + c$$
$$P = AB + BC + AC = 4 + 5 + 3 = 12$$

The perimeter of triangle ABC is 12 in.

Example 14

Strategy

To determine if the triangles are congruent, determine if one of the rules for congruence is satisfied.

Solution

$PR = MN$, $QR = MO$, and $\angle QRP = \angle OMN$.
The two sides and the included angle of one triangle equal two sides and the included angle of the other triangle.

The triangles are congruent by the SAS rule.

Example 16

Strategy

To determine if the triangles are congruent, draw a sketch of the two triangles and determine if one of the rules of congruence is satisfied.

Solution

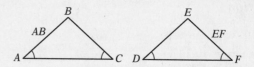

The triangles do not satisfy the SSS Rule, the SAS Rule, or the ASA Rule. The triangles are not necessarily congruent.

Section 4 *(pages 51 - 52)*

Example 2

Strategy

To find the circumference, use the circumference formula that involves the diameter. Leave the answer in terms of π.

Solution

$C = \pi d$
$C = \pi(9) = 9\pi$

The circumference is 9π in.

Example 4

Strategy

To find the area, use the formula for the area of a circle. An approximation is asked for; use the π key on a calculator. $r = 11$.

Solution

$A = \pi r^2 = \pi(11)^2 = 121\pi \approx 380.13$

The area is 380.13 cm².

Section 5 *(pages 55 - 60)*

Example 2

Strategy

To find the volume, use the formula for the volume of a cube.

Solution

$V = s^3$
$V = (2.5)^3 = 15.625$

The volume of the cube is 15.625 m³.

Example 4

Strategy

To find the volume:
▶ Find the radius of the base of the cylinder.
▶ Use the formula for the volume of a cylinder. Leave the answer in terms of π.

Solution

$r = \dfrac{1}{2}d = \dfrac{1}{2}(8) = 4$

$V = \pi r^2 h = \pi(4)^2(22) = \pi(16)(22) = 352\pi$

The volume of the cylinder is 352π ft².

Example 6

Strategy

To find the surface area of the cylinder:
► Find the radius of the base of the cylinder.
► Use the formula for the surface area of a cylinder. An approximation is asked for; use the π key on a calculator.

Solution

$$r = \frac{1}{2}d = \frac{1}{2}(6) = 3$$

$$SA = 2\pi r^2 + 2\pi rh$$
$$SA = 2\pi(3)^2 + 2\pi(3)(8)$$
$$= 2\pi(9) + 2\pi(24)$$
$$= 18\pi + 48\pi$$
$$= 66\pi$$
$$\approx 207.35$$

The surface area of the cylinder is 207.35 ft^2.

Example 8

Strategy

To find which solid has the larger surface area:
► Use the formula for the surface area of a cube to find the surface area of the cube.
► Find the radius of the sphere.
► Use the formula for the surface area of a sphere to find the surface area of the sphere. Since this number is to be compared to another number, use the π key on a calculator to approximate the surface area.
► Compare the two numbers.

Solution

$$SA = 6s^2 = 6(10)^2 = 6(100) = 600$$
    The surface area of the cube is 600 cm^2.

$$r = \frac{1}{2}d = \frac{1}{2}(8) = 4$$

$$SA = 4\pi r^2 = 4\pi(4)^2 = 4\pi(16) = 64\pi \approx 201.06$$
    The surface area of the sphere is 201.06 cm^2.

$$600 > 201.06$$

The cube has a larger surface area than the sphere.

Section 6 *(pages 65 - 68)*

Example 2

Strategy

To find the perimeter of square *ABCD*:
► Use the circumference formula that involves the diameter to find a diameter of the circle. A diameter of the circle is equal to the length of a side of the square.
► Use the formula for the perimeter of a square.

Solution

$$C = \pi d$$
$$6\pi = \pi d$$
$$6 = d \qquad \text{The diameter of the circle is 6 cm.}$$

$$P = 4s = 4(6) = 24$$

The perimeter of square *ABCD* is 24 cm.

Example 4

Strategy

The area is equal to the area of the rectangle minus the area of the triangle. The base of the triangle is equal to the width of the rectangle.

Solution

$$A = LW - \frac{1}{2}bh$$

$$A = 10(6) - \frac{1}{2}(6)(4) = 60 - 12 = 48$$

The area of the composite figure is 48 in^2.

Example 6

Strategy

The volume is equal to the volume of the rectangular solid plus the volume of the cylinder. Leave the answer in terms of π.

Solution

$V = LWH + \pi r^2 h$

$V = (8)(8)(2) + \pi(1)^2(2)$

$\quad = 128 + \pi(2) = 128 + 2\pi$

The volume of the solid is $(128 + 2\pi)$ cm^3.

Example 8

Strategy

The total surface area equals the surface area of the rectangular solid, minus the top of the rectangular solid, plus one-half the surface area of the cylinder. The radius of the base of the cylinder is one-half the width of the rectangular solid. The height of the cylinder is equal to the length of the rectangular solid. An approximation is asked for; use the π key on a calculator.

Solution

$r = \dfrac{1}{2}(W) = \dfrac{1}{2}(6) = 3$

$SA = LW + 2LH + 2WH + \dfrac{1}{2}(2\pi r^2 + 2\pi rh)$

$SA = (24)(6) + 2(24)(4) + 2(6)(4)$

$\qquad + \dfrac{1}{2}[2\pi(3)^2 + 2\pi(3)(24)]$

$\quad = 144 + 192 + 48 + \dfrac{1}{2}(18\pi + 144\pi)$

$\quad = 144 + 192 + 48 + \dfrac{1}{2}(162\pi)$

$\quad = 384 + 81\pi$

$\quad \approx 638.47$

The surface area of the solid is 638.47 in^2.

Answers to Odd-Numbered Exercises

Section 1 Exercises *(pages 13 - 18)*

1. 40°; acute   **3.** 115°; obtuse   **5.** 90°; right   **7.** 28°   **9.** 18°   **11.** 14 cm   **13.** 28 ft   **15.** 30 m
17. 86°   **19.** 71°   **21.** 30°   **23.** 36°   **25.** 127°   **27.** 116°   **29.** 20°   **31.** 20°   **33.** 20°
35. 141°   **37.** 106°   **39.** 11°   **41.** $\angle a = 38°, \angle b = 142°$ **43.** $\angle a = 47°, \angle b = 133°$ **45.** 20°
47. 47°   **49.** $\angle x = 155°, \angle y = 70°$ **51.** $\angle a = 45°, \angle b = 135°$ **53.** $90° - x$ **55.** 60°   **57.** 35°
59. 102°   **61.** 45°

Section 2 Exercises *(pages 29 - 34)*

1. Figure A   **3.** hexagon   **5.** pentagon   **7.** scalene   **9.** equilateral   **11.** obtuse   **13.** acute
15. 80°   **17.** 60°   **19.** 96°   **21.** 1,260°   **23.** 360°   **25.** 90°   **27.** 144°   **29.** 56 in.   **31.** 14 ft
33. 47 mi   **35.** 17.4 cm   **37.** 8 cm   **39.** 24 m   **41.** 48.8 cm   **43.** 17.5 in.   **45.** 60 ft   **47.** 44 ft
49. 120 ft   **51.** 10 in.   **53.** 12 in.   **55.** 2 packages   **57.** 60 ft^2 **59.** 20.25 in^2 **61.** 546 ft^2
63. 156.25 cm^2 **65.** 570 in^2 **67.** 192 in^2 **69.** 13.5 ft^2 **71.** 330 cm^2 **73.** 126 ft^2 **75.** 7,500 yd^2
77. 10 in.   **79.** 20 m   **81.** 6 m   **83.** 2 qt   **85.** $74   **87.** $638.00   **89.** 216 m^2

Section 3 Exercises *(pages 45 - 50)*

1. 5 in.   **3.** 8.6 cm   **5.** 11.2 ft   **7.** 4.5 cm   **9.** 12.7 yd   **11.** 6 ft, 6$\sqrt{3}$ ft   **13.** 15$\sqrt{2}$ cm   **15.** 8 m
17. 8$\sqrt{2}$ yd   **19.** 35.7 cm^2 **21.** 13.9 m^2 **23.** 8.5 cm   **25.** 24 in.   **27.** 14.2 ft   **29.** 17.1 in.
31. 8.5 in.   **33.** 10.9 cm   **35.** $\frac{1}{3}$ **37.** $\frac{1}{3}$ **39.** 13.7 in.   **41.** 4.9 ft   **43.** 38 cm   **45.** 45 cm^2
47. 49 m^2 **49.** 22.5 ft   **51.** 20.8 ft   **53.** 15 m   **55.** 8 ft   **57.** 12 m
59. The triangles are congruent by the ASA Rule.   **61.** The triangles are congruent by the SAS Rule.
63. The triangles are congruent by the SSS Rule.   **65.** Yes, the triangles are congruent by the SSS Rule.
67. Yes, the triangles are congruent by the ASA Rule.

Section 4 Exercises *(pages 53 - 54)*

1. The circumference is 8π cm or approximately 25.13 cm. The area is 16π cm^2 or approximately 50.27 cm^2.
3. The circumference is 11π mi or approximately 34.56 mi. The area is 30.25π mi^2 or approximately 95.03 mi^2.
5. The circumference is 17π ft or approximately 53.41 ft. The area is 72.25π ft^2 or approximately 226.98 ft^2.
7. 8.4 cm   **9.** 1.5π in.   **11.** 226.19 cm   **13.** 25π in^2 **15.** 9.08 ft^2 **17.** 2.55 cm   **19.** 13.19 ft
21. 50.27 ft   **23.** 39,935.93 km   **25.** 2,500π ft^2 **27.** 339.29 cm^2

Section 5 Exercises *(pages 61 - 64)*

1. 840 in^3 **3.** 15 ft^3 **5.** 4.5π cm^3 or approximately 14.14 cm^3 **7.** 34 m^3 **9.** 15.625 in^3 **11.** 36π ft^3
13. 8,143.01 cm^3 **15.** 75π in^3 **17.** 120 in^3 **19.** 2.5 ft   **21.** 4.00 in.   **23.** length: 5 in.; width: 5 in.
25. 75.40 m^3 **27.** The volume is quadrupled (multiplied by 4).   **29.** 94 m^2 **31.** 56 m^2
33. 96π in^2 or approximately 301.59 in^2 **35.** 184 ft^2 **37.** 69.36 m^2 **39.** 225π cm^2 **41.** 402.12 in^2
43. 6π ft^2 **45.** 297 in^2 **47.** 3 cm   **49.** 11 cans of paint   **51.** 3,217 ft^2 **53.** 898.22 cm^2
55. The surface area is quadrupled (multiplied by 4).

Section 6 Exercises *(pages 69 - 74)*

1. 121 cm   **3.** (2π + 4) ft or approximately 10.28 ft   **5.** (4π + 38) m or approximately 50.57 m   **7.** 176 ft
9. (π + 4) ft or approximately 7.14 ft   **11.** 22.9 m   **13.** 20.71 ft   **15.** $9,360   **17.** 26 cm^2

19. $(4.5\pi + 36)$ in^2 or approximately 50.14 in^2 **21.** 48π in^2 or approximately 150.80 in^2 **23.** 30 in^2
25. 16 in^2 **27.** $(12.5\pi + 25\sqrt{3})$ in^2 or approximately 82.57 in^2 **29.** \$640.10   **31.** 19,026.55 ft^2
33. $(1.92 - 0.08\pi)$ m^3 or approximately 1.67 m^3 **35.** 126π ft^3 or approximately 395.84 ft^3 **37.** 272 ft^3
39. 8.25π in^3 or approximately 25.92 in^3 **41.** 36π in^3 or approximately 113.10 in^3
43. 1,458π cm^3 or approximately 4,580.44 cm^3 **45.** 212.60 in^3 **47.** \$3,515.00   **49.** 19 m^2
51. 93π cm^2 or approximately 292.17 cm^2 **53.** $(160\pi + 120)$ m^2 or approximately 622.65 m^2
55. 56π cm^2 or approximately 175.93 cm^2 **57.** 324 ft^2 **59.** $(15\pi + 126)$ in^2 or approximately 173.12 in^2
61. 158 cans of paint   **63.** \$498.75

Review Exercises *(pages 77 - 78)*

1. $\angle x = 22°$, $\angle y = 158°$ (Objective 1A)   **2.** The triangles are congruent by the SAS Rule (Objective 3C)
3. 240 in^3 (Objective 6C)   **4.** 68° (Objective 1A)   **5.** 8 ft (Objective 3A)   **6.** 138.23 m^2 (Objective 6D)
7. 10.4π cm (Objective 4A)   **8.** 9.75 ft (Objective 3A)   **9.** 57.13 in^2 (Objective 6B)   **10.** 96 cm^3 (Objective 5A)
11. 47.71 in. (Objective 6A)   **12.** $\angle a = 138°$, $\angle b = 42°$ (Objective 1B)   **13.** 24 in. (Objective 3B)
14. 19° (Objective 1A)   **15.** 220 ft^2 (Objective 5B)   **16.** 63.62 cm^2 (Objective 4A)   **17.** 148° (Objective 1A)
18. 140° (Objective 2A)   **19.** 95° (Objective 1C)   **20.** 8 cm (Objective 2C)   **21.** 14.14 in. (Objective 3A)
22. 4 cans of paint (Objective 5B)   **23.** 208 yd (Objective 2B)   **24.** 90.25 m^2 (Objective 2C)

INDEX